TEACHING

An Introduction to the Profession

Reflections • Activities • Resources

D1507364

South Jersey Teacher Education Consortium

Rowan University
Atlantic Cape Community College
Camden County College
Cumberland County College
Gloucester County College
Salem Community College

Frank J. Orlando

Grateful acknowledgment is made to the following sources for permission to reprint material copyrighted or controlled by them:
"Toward a Philosophy of Education," by Donald P. Kauchak, Paul D. Eggen, and Candice Carter, reprinted from *Introduction to Teaching: Becoming a Professional*, (2001), by permission of Prentice-Hall, Inc.
"How Have Supreme Court Decisions Affected the Public Schools," copyright © 2001 Allyn and Bacon.
"Selections from Dr. LeBaeu's Web Site," reprinted from *www.suelebeau.com*, by Dr. Sue LeBeau.

Printed in the United States of America

10 9 8 7 6 5 4

ISBN 0-536-10179-5

2005220122

EM/SM

Please visit our web site at *www.pearsoncustom.com*

PEARSON CUSTOM PUBLISHING
75 Arlington Street, Suite 300, Boston, MA 02116
A Pearson Education Company

CONTENTS

Chapter 3 - Learner Diversity

Chapter 4 - Changes in American Society

Chapter 5 - Educational Philosophy

Chapter 6 - The Organization of American Schools

Chapter 7 - School Law

Chapter 8 - The School Curriculum

Chapter 9 - Instruction in American Classrooms

Chapter 10 - Joining the Profession

Chapter 11 - Traditional Educational Technology

Chapter 12 - Contemporary Educational Technology

Chapter 13 - Teaching in New Jersey

Appendix

To The Student

This manual is designed to accompany the textbook *Teaching: An Introduction to the Profession* by Frank J. Orlando, D. Mark Meyers. Joseph J. Pizzillo, and Lynne C. Levy.

The major portion of this manual consists of a set of materials for each of the first thirteen chapters in the text. Each set includes the following items:

1. A form for class reflections
2. Chapter-related activities
3. Resource materials to supplement the chapter content

The Appendix includes:
1. A Student Information Form
2. Six Class Observation Note Forms
3. An Observation Symposium Worksheet

Chapter 1

Why Become A Teacher?

Name_____

CLASS REFLECTIONS - Why Become A Teacher?

....

Date:_____   Topic:_____

Description:

_____

_____

_____

_____

_____

Analysis:

_____

_____

_____

_____

_____

Future Impact:

_____

_____

_____

_____

_____

_____

Date:_____ Topic:_____

Description:

_____

_____

_____

_____

_____

Analysis:

_____

_____

_____

_____

_____

Future Impact:

_____

_____

_____

_____

_____

Name_____

Activity 1.1 - Review for Chapter 1

I. Clearly explain or define the following terms, concepts, or acronyms.

- extrinsic rewards:

- high-stakes tests:

- intrinsic rewards:

- NEA:

- standards-based education:

II. Identify three reasons people choose to teach in a private school.

1.

2.

3.

III. Identify three characteristics of a profession.

    1.

    2.

    3.

IV. Identify and discuss two recent changes that have taken place regarding the preparation of teachers.

    1.

    2.

Name_____

Activity 1.2 - Teachers Under the Microscope

When an individual decides to pursue a career in the field of education, in many cases there is a former teacher who either directly or indirectly played a role in that decision. Of even greater importance is the fact that our individual teaching styles and attitudes are greatly influenced by the teaching we encounter. The saying "We teach as we are taught" is as true today as it was when it was first stated.

Respond to the following three questions and be prepared to discuss them. <u>Do not use the names of people anywhere in your responses</u>.

ONE - Think about the various teachers you have encountered in elementary school, high school, college, or even in informal teaching situations. Try to recall the two best teachers, whether you had them for a year, a semester, or even a single class period. In the space below tell why these two individuals were so exceptional.

<u>Teacher One</u>:

<u>Teacher Two</u>:

TWO - In addition to having teachers who represent the best of the profession, you have probably encountered teachers who either were not professionally prepared as a teacher or did not exhibit the best traits of an effective teacher. Think about your educational experiences with two such individuals. In the space below tell why these individuals were not effective teachers.

Teacher One:

Teacher Two:

THREE - Now that you have critically examined other educators, fast-forward to the future where you are a teacher. Your students have been asked to identify why you are an exceptional teacher. What would you like them to be able to say?

Activity 1.3 - Teaching: Rewards and Challenges

1. In what type of school or at what grade level do you want to teach?

    _____ Elementary School (P-4)

    _____ Middle School (5-8)

    _____ High School (9-12)

2. Think about the video segment you viewed regarding teaching and/or recall some of the classes you were in, and teachers you had, at the level you have selected.

3. Identify three rewards and three challenges of being a teacher at the level selected.

Rewards:

1.

2.

3.

Challenges:

1.

2.

3.

Resource 1.1

Rules for Teachers: 1872 & 1915

1872

1. Teachers each day will fill lamps, clean chimneys.

2. Each teacher will bring a bucket of water and a scuttle of coal for the day's session.

3. Make your pens carefully. You may whittle nibs to the individual taste of the pupils.

4. Men teachers may take one evening each week for courting purposes or two evenings a week if they go to church regularly.

5. After ten hours in school, teachers may spend the remaining time reading the Bible or other good books.

6. Women teachers who marry or engage in unseemly conduct will be dismissed.

7. Each teacher should lay aside from each day pay a goodly sum of his earnings for his benefit during his declining years so that he will not become a burden on society.

8. Any teacher who smokes, uses liquor in any form, frequents pool or public halls, or gets shaved in a barber shop will give good reason to suspect his worth, intention, integrity and honesty.

9. The teacher who performs his labor faithfully and without fault for five years will be given an increase of twenty-five cents per week in his pay, providing the Board of Education approves.

- The Oldest Wooden Schoolhouse
St. Augustine, Florida

1915

1. You may not marry during the term of your contract.

2. You are not to keep company with men.

3. You must be home between the hours of 8 p.m. and 6 a.m. unless attending a school function.

4. You may not loiter downtown in ice cream stores.

5. You may not travel beyond city limits unless you have the permission of the chairman of the board.

6. You may not ride in a carriage or automobile with any man unless he is your father or brother.

7. You may not smoke cigarettes.

8. You may not dress in bright colors.

9. You may under no circumstances dye your hair.

10. You must wear at least two petticoats.

11. Your dresses must not be any shorter that two inches above the ankle.

12. To keep the school room neat and clean, you must:

    -   sweep the floor at least once daily
    -   scrub the floor at least once a week with hot soapy water
    -   clean the blackboards at least once a day
    -   start the fire at 7 a.m. so the room will be warm by 8 a.m.

Resource 1.2

2004-2005 Salary Data for Teachers in Gloucester County

District	Beginning Salary	Top Salary
Clayton	$35,039	$65,315
Clearview Regional	$38,000	$74,814
Delsea	$40,350	$67,896
Deptford	$41,000	$73,850
East Greenwich	$37,200	$63,808
Elk	$35,835	$65,908
Franklin	$37,600	$67,500
Gateway Regional	$38,950	$68,428
Glassboro	$38,152	$71,851
Greater Egg Harbor	$40,400	$74,705
Greenwich	$38,956	$75,437
Harrison	$38,035	$63,095
Kingsway Regional	$38,476	$69,217
Logan	$41,004	$70,102
Mantua	$36,595	$62,780
Monroe	$41,400	$72,150
National Park	$37,000	$66,300
Paulsboro	$34,039	$68,259

District	Beginning Salary	Top Salary
Pitman	$38,446	$71,348
South Harrison	$35,890	$59,250
Swedesboro-Woolwich	$35,220	$65,609
Washington Township	$39,216	$70,700
Wenonah	$37,000	$65,800
West Deptford	$41,780	$68,120
Westville	$37,000	$68,000
Woodbury	$40,000	$75,150
Woodbury Heights	$38,800	$72,150

Chapter 2

The Teaching Profession

Name_____

CLASS REFLECTIONS - The Teaching Profession

....

Date:_____   Topic:_____

Description:

_____

_____

_____

_____

_____

Analysis:

_____

_____

_____

_____

_____

_____

Future Impact:

_____

_____

_____

_____

_____

_____

....

Date:_____   Topic:_____

Description:

_____

_____

_____

_____

_____

Analysis:

_____

_____

_____

_____

_____

Future Impact:

_____

_____

_____

_____

_____

20

Name_____

Activity 2.1 - Review for Chapter 2

I. Explain or define the meaning of the following terms, concepts or acronyms.

• Block Scheduling:

• Reflective Practitioner:

• Year-round Schooling

II. Briefly discuss the following five dimensions of teaching.

1. Multidimensional:

2. Simultaneous:

3. Immediate:

4. Unpredictable:

5. Public:

III. Identify the following information regarding the teachers you had for courses as a senior in high school.

1. Total number of teachers you were assigned to as a senior: _____

2. Of this number, how many were males? _____

3. Of this number, how many were females? _____

4. How many of the males were under 30 years of age? _____

5. How many of the males were 30 to 60 years of age? _____

6. How many of the males were older than 60? _____

7. How many of the females were under 30 years of age? _____

8. How many of the females were 30 to 60 years of age? _____

9. How many of the females were older than 60? _____

Name_____

Activity 2.2 - Roles in the Educational Structure

Check one of the following grade ranges and identify four major duties or responsibilities for each of the following groups.

_____Grades K-4   _____Grades 5-6   _____Grades 7-8   _____Grades 9-12

Teachers are expected to:

1._____

_____

2._____

_____

3._____

_____

4._____

_____

Students are expected to:

1._____

_____

2._____

_____

3._____

_____

4._____

_____

School Administrators are expected to:

1._____

_____

2._____

_____

3._____

_____

4._____

_____

Resource 2.1
The New Jersey Professional Standards for Teachers:
An Introduction

On July 1, 2004, the New Jersey Department of Education released New *Jersey Professional Standards for Teachers and School Leaders.* The following pages are taken from that publication.

Introduction

New Jersey's new professional standards for teachers and school leaders were adopted by the State Board of Education in December 2003 as part of the new licensing regulations. These new professional standards provide a clear vision of the knowledge, performances, and dispositions that teachers and school leaders need to support the learning called for in the revised Core Curriculum Content Standards.

Aligned with the Core Curriculum Content Standards, as well as national professional standards, New Jersey's professional standards for educators illustrate the wide range of knowledge and abilities contemporary educators must possess to provide high-quality instruction and support improved student results.

While the sets of professional standards are interdependent and interconnected, each distinct standard focuses on a specific aspect of effective practice. Each standard also has a series of indicators comprised of knowledge, dispositions, and performance statements. The knowledge statements describe the body of knowledge critical to effective practice. The disposition statements indicate the behaviors which communicate the traits and qualities valued by educators. The performance statements illustrate the application of that knowledge.

Professional Standards for Teachers

Research conducted over the past decade by groups such as the National Commission on Teaching and America's Future and the Center for the Improvement of Early Reading Achievement have identified a knowledge base and the skill sets that successful teachers possess. While teaching will always be a balance between an art and a craft, there is significant data now about the skills and knowledge which bring success.

The New Jersey Professional Standards for Teachers were developed by the New Jersey Professional Teaching Standards Board (PTSB). The PTSB worked closely with national experts from the Interstate New Teacher Assessment Support

Consortium (INTASC) of the Council of Chief State School Officers, the organization that developed the national model for professional standards for teachers. The PTSB also incorporated broad input from New Jersey educators. As a result, the standards emphasize skills not present in the national INTASC model that are nonetheless important to New Jersey educators, such as a concern for teaching literacy and numeracy across the curriculum and the use of technology in instruction.

These standards encompass the broad range of skills and knowledge a teacher needs, including deep content knowledge with varied instructional strategies; the creation of a productive learning environment; the use of assorted assessments; the understanding of human growth; the ability to work with diverse learners; strong communication skills; instructional planning; and the ability to create strong partnerships with parents, colleges, and the community. The standards also place an emphasis on reading and mathematics, because of the heightened expectations for these two areas sought by Governor McGreevey's initiatives and the *No Child Left Behind Act.*

The contemporary job of the teacher is exceedingly complex, requiring a wide array of knowledge and skills.

The professional standards serve as the foundation for a more thoughtful certification system, more productive pre-service education and induction programs, and more effective and relevant professional development.

New Jersey Professional Standards for Teachers
Standard One • Subject Matter Knowledge

Teachers shall understand the central concepts, tools of inquiry, structures of the discipline, especially as they relate to the New Jersey Core Curriculum Content Standards (CCCS), and design developmentally appropriate learning experiences making the subject matter accessible and meaningful to all students.

• KNOWLEDGE •

Teachers know and understand:

1.1 In-depth the subject matter they plan to teach and the relationship of that discipline to other content areas;

1.2 The evolving nature of the discipline or subject matter knowledge and the need for keeping abreast of new ideas and understanding of the discipline;

1.3 That literacy skills and processes are applicable in all content areas and help students to develop the knowledge, skills and dispositions that enable them to construct meaning and make sense of the world through reading, writing, listening, speaking and viewing; and

1.4 Concepts inherent in numeracy to enable students to represent physical events, work with data, reason, communicate mathematically, and make connections within their respective content areas in order to solve problems.

• DISPOSITIONS •

Teachers value and are committed to:

1.5 Appreciating multiple perspectives and conveying to learners how knowledge is developed from the vantage point of the knower; and

1.6 Enthusiasm for the discipline(s) they teach and in making connections to every day life.

• PERFORMANCES •

Teachers engage in activities to:

1.7 Promote the development of critical and creative thinking, problem-solving and decision-making skills by engaging students in formulating and testing hypotheses according to the methods of inquiry and standards of evidence within the discipline;

1.8 Make effective use of multiple representations and explanations of disciplinary concepts that capture key ideas and link them to students' prior understanding; and

1.9 Evaluate teaching resources and curriculum materials for their completeness, accuracy and usefulness for representing particular ideas and concepts.

New Jersey Professional Standards for Teachers
Standard Two • Human Growth and Development

Teachers shall understand how children and adolescents develop and learn in a variety of school, family and community contexts and provide opportunities that support their intellectual, social, emotional and physical development.

• KNOWLEDGE •

Teachers know and understand:

2.1   How students construct knowledge, acquire skills and develop habits of mind and how to use instructional strategies that promote student learning;

2.2   How student learning is influenced by individual experiences, talents and prior learning, as well as language, culture, family, and community values; and

2.3   How to identify and teach to the developmental abilities of students, which may include learning differences, visual and perceptual differences, cultural and socio-emotional differences, special physical or emotional challenges and gifted and talented exceptionalities.

• DISPOSITIONS •

Teachers value and are committed to:

2.4   The educability of all children and adolescents;

2.5   The belief that all children and adolescents bring talents and strengths to learning;

2.6   Appreciation for multiple ways of knowing;

2.7   The diverse talents of all students and to helping them develop self-confidence and subject matter competence; and

2.8   The belief that all children and adolescents can learn at high levels and achieve success.

• PERFORMANCES •

Teachers apply:

2.9   Learning theory to accommodate differences in student intelligence, perception, cognitive style and achievement levels.

New Jersey Professional Standards for Teachers
Standard Three • Diverse Learners

Teachers shall understand the practice of culturally responsive teaching.

• KNOWLEDGE •

Teachers know and understand:
3.1   How a person's world view is profoundly shaped by his or her life experiences, as mediated by factors such as social class, gender, race, ethnicity, language, sexual orientation, age and special needs;
3.2   The supports for and barriers to culturally responsive teaching in school environments;
3.3   The process of second language acquisition and strategies to support the learning of students whose first language is not English; and
3.4   The negative impact of bias, prejudice, and discrimination on students and society.

• DISPOSITIONS •

Teachers value and are committed to:
3.5   Respect for individual and cultural differences, and appreciation of the basic worth of each individual and cultural group; and
3.6   The diversity of learning that takes place in the classroom, respect for the talents and perspectives of each student and sensitivity to community and cultural norms.

• PERFORMANCES •

Teachers engage in activities to:
3.7   Create a learning community in which individual differences are respected;
3.8   Learn about the diverse students they teach, and the students' families and communities;
3.9   Use strategies to support the learning of students whose first language is not English; and
3.10   Use knowledge of students and their lives to design and carry out instruction that   builds on students' strengths while meeting their needs and taking into account issues of social class, gender, race, ethnicity, language, sexual orientation, age and special needs.

New Jersey Professional Standards for Teachers
Standard Four • Instructional Planning and Strategies

Teachers shall understand instructional planning, design long- and short-term plans based upon knowledge of subject matter, students, community, and curriculum goals, and shall employ a variety of developmentally appropriate strategies in order to promote critical thinking, problem solving and the performance skills of all learners.

• KNOWLEDGE •

Teachers know and understand:

4.1   How to plan instruction based on students' needs, developmental progress and prior knowledge;

4.2   Available and appropriate resources and materials for instructional planning;

4.3   Techniques for modifying instructional methods, materials and the environment to help all students learn; and

4.4   A variety of instructional approaches and the use of various technologies, to promote thinking and understanding.

• DISPOSITIONS •

Teachers value and are committed to:

4.5   The development of students' critical thinking, independent problem-solving and performance capabilities.

• PERFORMANCES •

Teachers engage in activities to:

4.6   Identify and design instruction appropriate to students' stage of development, learning styles, strengths and needs;

4.7   Plan instruction based on knowledge of classroom, school and community culture;

4.8   Evaluate teaching resources and curriculum materials for their comprehensiveness, accuracy and usefulness for representing particular ideas and concepts;

4.9   Identify strategies to create learning experiences that make subject matter meaningful for students, address a variety of learning styles, encourage students to pursue their own interests and inquiries and help students connect their learning to personal goals;

4.10   Plan and develop effective lessons by organizing instructional activities and materials, incorporating a wide range of community and technology resources, to promote achievement of lesson objectives;

4.11   Use formal and informal methods of assessment, information about students, pedagogical knowledge, and research as sources for active reflection, evaluation and revision of practice; and

4.12   Create interdisciplinary learning experiences that allow students to integrate knowledge, skills and methods of inquiry from several subject areas.

New Jersey Professional Standards for Teachers
Standard Five • Assessment

Teachers shall understand and use multiple assessment strategies and interpret results to evaluate and promote student learning and to modify instruction in order to foster the continuous development of students.

• KNOWLEDGE •

Teachers know and understand:

5.1   The characteristics, uses, advantages, and limitations of different types of assessments (for example, criterion-referenced and norm-referenced instruments, traditional standardized and performance- based tests, observation systems and assessments of student work) for evaluating how students learn, what they know and are able to do, and what kinds of experiences will support their further growth and development; and

5.2   Measurement theory and assessment-related issues, such as validity, reliability, bias and scoring concerns.

• DISPOSITIONS •

Teachers value and are committed to:

5.3   The belief that students' strengths are the basis for growth and their errors are opportunities for learning.

• PERFORMANCES •

Teachers engage in activities to:

5.4   Analyze student performance using multiple sources of data, and to modify future plans and instructional techniques that promote desired student learning outcomes;

5.5   Provide students with constructive feedback on their learning and encourage their use of data and self-assessment strategies to monitor their progress toward personal goals;

5.6   Accurately document and report assessment data and ongoing student data to parents and professional staff; and

5.7   Enhance their knowledge of learners and evaluate students' progress and performance using a variety of formal and informal assessment techniques to modify teaching and learning strategies.areas.

New Jersey Professional Standards for Teachers
Standard Six • Learning Environment

Teachers shall understand individual and group motivation and behavior and shall create a supportive, safe and respectful learning environment that encourages positive social interaction, active engagement in learning and self-motivation.

• KNOWLEDGE •

Teachers know and understand:

6.1 The principles and strategies of effective classroom management that promote positive relationships, cooperation and purposeful learning activities in the classroom;

6.2 How the classroom environment influences learning and promotes positive behavior for all students; and

6.3 How classroom participation supports student commitment.

• DISPOSITIONS •

Teachers value and are committed to:

6.4 The role of students in promoting each other's learning and recognize the importance of peer relationships in creating a climate of learning;

6.5 Taking responsibility for establishing a positive climate in the classroom and participation in maintaining such a climate in the school as a whole; and

6.6 The expression and use of democratic values in the classroom.

• PERFORMANCES •

Teachers engage in activities to:

6.7 Maintain a learning community in which students assume responsibility for themselves and one another, participate in decision-making and work collaboratively and independently;

6.8 Create a safe and secure classroom climate for all students, by practicing effective listening and group facilitation skills;

6.9 Create a positive classroom climate which is socially, emotionally and physically safe;

6.10 Establish and maintain appropriate standards of behavior;

6.11 Use instructional time effectively; and

6.12 Prepare students for and monitor independent and group work that allows for full and varied participation of all individuals.

New Jersey Professional Standards for Teachers
Standard Seven • Special Needs

Teachers shall adapt and modify instruction to accommodate the special learning needs of all students.

• KNOWLEDGE •

Teachers know and understand:

7.1   How to access information regarding applicable laws, rules, regulations and procedural safeguards regarding planning and implementing the individual education program; and

7.2   Available resources related to educational strategies to accommodate individual differences and to employ positive behavioral intervention techniques to students with special needs.

• DISPOSITIONS •

Teachers value and are committed to:

7.3   The belief that children and adolescents with special needs can learn at high levels and achieve success.

• PERFORMANCES •

Teachers engage in activities to:

7.4   Apply knowledge of students' abilities/disabilities, experiences, talents and prior learning, as well as language, culture, economics, family and community values to positively impact student learning;

7.5   Employ appropriate diagnostic measures and interpret the results to implement strategies that influence learning;

7.6   Participate in the design and implementation of the Individualized Education Program (IEP), where appropriate;

7.7   Meet the needs of all learners by using a wide range of teaching techniques to accommodate and modify strategies, services and resources, including technology; and

7.8   Make appropriate provisions, in terms of time and circumstances, for work, task assigned, communication and response modes, for individual students who have particular learning differences or needs.

New Jersey Professional Standards for Teachers
Standard Eight • Communication

Teachers shall use knowledge of effective verbal, nonverbal and written communication techniques and the tools of information literacy to foster the use of inquiry, collaboration and supportive interactions.

• KNOWLEDGE •

Teachers know and understand:
8.1   The power of communication in the teaching and learning process.

• DISPOSITIONS •

Teachers value and are committed to:
8.2   Appreciating the cultural dimension of communication, responding appropriately and seeking to foster culturally sensitive communication by and among all students in the class; and
8.3   Being a thoughtful and responsive listener.

• PERFORMANCES •

Teachers engage in activities to:
8.4   Communicate clearly in English, using precise language and appropriate oral and written expressions;
8.5   Assist students individually or as a member of a group to access, evaluate, synthesize and use information effectively to accomplish a specific purpose;
8.6   Use effective verbal and nonverbal techniques which foster individual and collective inquiry;
8.7   Model effective communication strategies and questioning techniques in conveying ideas and stimulating critical thinking; and
8.8   Communicate in a variety of ways that demonstrate a sensitivity to cultural, linguistic, gender and social differences.

New Jersey Professional Standards for Teachers
Standard Nine • Collaboration and Partnerships

Teachers shall build relationships with parents, guardians, families and agencies in the larger community to support students' learning and well-being.

• KNOWLEDGE •

Teachers know and understand:

9.1 The importance of meaningful parent/family involvement in education in addressing the unique student needs and the perspectives to be gained from effective school/home interactions that contribute to high-quality teaching and learning;

9.2 The role of the school within the community and how to utilize diverse partnerships to contribute to student learning and development; and

9.3 How to collaborate with all stakeholders regarding decision-making and the well-being of students while respecting student/family privacy and confidentiality.

• DISPOSITIONS •

Teachers value and are committed to:

9.4 Recognizing the role of parents, guardians and other family members as a child's primary teacher;

9.5 Being concerned about all aspects of the student's well-being and working with parents/families to provide diverse opportunities for student success; and

9.6 Being willing to work with parents/families and other professionals to improve the overall learning environment for students.

• PERFORMANCES •

Teachers engage in activities to:

9.7 Identify and utilize family and community resources to foster student learning and provide opportunities for parents to share skills and talents that enrich learning experiences;

9.8 Establish respectful and productive relationships and to develop cooperative partnerships with diverse families, educators and others in the community in support of student learning and wellbeing; and

9.9 Institute parent/family involvement practices that support meaningful communication, parenting skills, enriched student learning, volunteer and decision-making opportunities at school and collaboration to strengthen the teaching and learning environment of the school.

New Jersey Professional Standards for Teachers
Standard Ten • Professional Development

Teachers shall participate as active, responsible members of the professional community, engaging in a wide range of reflective practices, pursuing opportunities to grow professionally and establishing collegial relationships to enhance the teaching and learning process.

• KNOWLEDGE •

Teachers know and understand:

10.1   How education research and other methods of inquiry can be used as a means for continuous learning, self assessment and development.

• DISPOSITIONS •

Teachers value and are committed to:

10.2   Refining practices that address the needs of all students and the school community;

10.3   Professional reflection, assessment and learning as an ongoing process; and

10.4   Collaboration with colleagues to give and receive help.

• PERFORMANCES •

Teachers engage in activities to:

10.5   Use reflective practice and the Professional Development Standards to set goals for their professional development plans;

10.6   Learn through professional education organizations; and

10.7   Make the entire school a productive learning climate through participation in collegial activities.

Chapter 3

Learner Diversity

Name_____

CLASS REFLECTIONS - Learner Diversity

....

Date:_____   Topic:_____

Description:

_____

_____

_____

_____

_____

Analysis:

_____

_____

_____

_____

_____

Future Impact:

_____

_____

_____

_____

_____

....

Date:_____   Topic:_____

Description:

_____

_____

_____

_____

_____

Analysis:

_____

_____

_____

_____

_____

Future Impact:

_____

_____

_____

_____

_____

TEACHING: Name_____
An Introduction
to the Profession

Activity 3.1 - Review for Chapter 3

I. Explain or define the meaning of the following terms, concepts or acronyms.

• Culturally Responsive Teaching:

• Culture:

• ESL:

• Ethnicity:

• Exceptionalities:

• Immersion Programs:

• LDs

• Least Restrictive Environment:

• Multicultural Education:

• Multiple Intelligences:

• Tracking:

II. The following statement is taken from the text. Does this statement agree with what you observed in your schooling? Explain.

Boys outnumber girls in remedial English and math classes, are held back a grade more often, and are two to three times more likely to be placed in special-education classes.

Activity 3.2 - Your Preferred Learning Style

Part One – Gardner's "Intelligences"

Using the following chart, rate your preferences regarding Howard Gardner's eight "intelligences" or learning styles. Five (5) means "strongly favors" and one (1) means "dislikes."

1. **Verbal-Linguistic**
   - sensitive to words
   - varied uses of language
	5	4	3	2	1

2. **Logical-Mathematical**
   - enjoys reasoning and logic
   - recognizes patterns
	5	4	3	2	1

3. **Visual-Spatial**
   - accurately perceive the visual
   - can modify the visual perception
	5	4	3	2	1

4. **Body-Kinesthetic**
   - ability to use the body
   - enjoys physical activity
	5	4	3	2	1

5. **Musical-Rhythmic**
   - sensitivity to pitch and tone
   - can create melodies
	5	4	3	2	1

6. **Interpersonal**
   - understand interpersonal relations
   - ability to make distinctions
	5	4	3	2	1

7. **Intrapersonal**
   - understands one's self
   - self analysis
	5	4	3	2	1

8. **Naturalists**
   - understands the physical world
   - comfortable in the natural world
	5	4	3	2	1

Part Two – Your Preferred Learning Environment

In approximately 125 words, describe an ideal learning environment FOR YOU, if you were a student in an 11th grade science or 11th grade social studies class. Check the subject area you have chosen.

_____11th grade science   _____11th grade social studies

Name_____

Activity 3.3 - Special Needs in the Classroom

All teachers will have students in their classes that will require special attention and planning. (These are usually referred to as "accommodations" and "modifications.")

Select <u>any three</u> of the following six special needs concerns and briefly tell how you could address this issue.

1. Visual Disability

2. Learning Disability

3. Hearing Impairment

4. Physical Disability

5. Mental Retardation

6. Behavioral Disability

Resource 3.1

Overview of ADA, IDEA, and Section 504
Kelly Henderson
(ERIC Digest E606)

• **AMERICANS WITH DISABILITIES ACT OF 1990 (ADA)**

Type/Purpose

A civil rights law to prohibit discrimination solely on the basis of disability in employment, public services, and accommodations.

Who is Eligible?

Any individual with a disability who: (1) has a physical or mental impairment that substantially limits one or more life activities; or (2) has a record of such an impairment; or (3) is regarded as having such an impairment. Further, the person must be qualified for the program, service or job.

Responsibility to Provide a Free, Appropriate Public Education (FAPE)?

Not directly. However, ADA provides additional protection in combination with actions brought under Section 504 and IDEA. ADA protections apply to nonsectarian private schools, but not to organizations or entities controlled by religious organizations. Reasonable accommodations are required for eligible students with a disability to perform essential functions of the job. This applies to any part of the special education program that may be community-based and involve job training/placement. Although not required, an IEP under IDEA will fulfill requirements of Title II of the ADA for an appropriate education for a student with disabilities.

Funding to Implement Requirements?

No, but limited tax credits may be available for removing architectural or transportation barriers. Also, many federal agencies provide grants to public and private institutions to support training and technical assistance.

Procedural Safeguards/Due Process

The ADA does not specify procedural safeguards related to special education; it does detail the administrative requirements, complaint procedures, and consequences for noncompliance related to both services and employment. The

ADA also does not delineate specific due process procedures. People with disabilities have the same remedies that are available under Title VII of the Civil Rights Act of 1964, as amended by the Civil Rights Act of 1991. Thus, individuals who are discriminated against may file a complaint with the relevant federal agency or sue in federal court. Enforcement agencies encourage informal mediation and voluntary compliance.

Evaluation/Placement Procedures

The ADA does not specify evaluation and placement procedures; it does specify provision of reasonable accommodations for eligible students across educational activities and settings. Reasonable accommodations may include, but are not limited to, redesigning equipment, assigning aides, providing written communication in alternative formats, modifying tests, reassigning services to accessible locations, altering existing facilities, and building new facilities.

• INDIVIDUALS WITH DISABILITIES EDUCATION ACT (IDEA), AMENDED IN 1997

Type/Purpose

An education act to provide federal financial assistance to state and local education agencies to guarantee special education and related services to eligible children with disabilities.

Who is Eligible?

Children and youth aged 3-21 who are determined through an individualized evaluation and by a multidisciplinary team (including the parent) to be eligible in one or more of 13 categories and who need special education and related services. The categories are autism, deaf-blindness, deafness, emotional disturbance, hearing impairment, mental retardation, multiple disabilities, orthopedic impairment, other health impairment, specific learning disability, speech or language impairment, traumatic brain injury, and visual impairment including blindness. Children aged 3 through 9 experiencing developmental delays may also be eligible. Infants and toddlers from birth through age 2 may be eligible for early intervention services, delivered in accordance with an individualized family service plan.

Responsibility To Provide a Free, Appropriate Public Education (FAPE)?

Yes. A FAPE is defined to mean special education and related services that are provided at no charge to parents, meet other state educational standards, and are consistent with an individualized educational program (IEP). Special education means "specially designed instruction, at no cost to the parents, to meet the unique needs of the child with a disability." Related services are those required to assist a child to benefit from special education, including speech- language pathology, physical and occupational therapy, and others. A team of professionals and parents develop and review at least annually, an IEP for each child with a disability. IDEA requires certain content in the IEP.

Funding To Implement Requirements?

Yes. IDEA provides federal funds under Parts B and C to assist state and local educational agencies in meeting IDEA requirements to serve infants, toddlers, children, and youth with disabilities.

Procedural Safeguards/Due Process

IDEA provides for procedural safeguards and due process rights to parents in the identification, evaluation and educational placement of their child. Prior written notice of procedural safeguards and of proposals or refusals to initiate or change identification, evaluation, or placement must be provided to parents. IDEA delineates the required components of these notices. Disputes may be resolved through mediation, impartial due process hearings, appeal of hearing decisions, and/or civil action.

Evaluation/Placement Procedures

With parental consent, an individualized evaluation must be conducted using a variety of technically sound, unbiased assessment tools. Based on the results, a team of professionals (including the parent of the child) determines eligibility for special education. Reevaluations are conducted at least every 3 years. Results are used to develop an IEP that specifies the special education, related services, and supplemental aids and services to be provided to address the child's goals. Placement in the least restrictive environment (LRE) is selected from a continuum of alternative placements, based on the child's IEP, and reviewed at least annually. IEPs must be reviewed at least annually to see whether annual goals are being met. IDEA contains specific provisions about IEP team composition, parent participation, IEP content, and consideration of special factors.

• SECTION 504 OF THE REHABILITATION ACT OF 1973

Type/Purpose

A civil rights law to prohibit discrimination on the basis of disability in programs and activities, public and private, that receive federal financial assistance.

Who Is Eligible?

Any person who: (1) has a physical or mental impairment that substantially limits one or more major life activities, (2) has a record of such an impairment, or (3) is regarded as having such an impairment. Major life activities include caring for oneself, performing manual tasks, walking, seeing, hearing, speaking, breathing, learning, and working. The person must be qualified for the services or job; in the case of school services, the person must be of an age when non-disabled peers are typically served or be eligible under IDEA.

Responsibility To Provide a Free, Appropriate Public Education (FAPE)?

Yes. An "appropriate" education means an education comparable to that provided to students without disabilities. This may be regular or special education. Students can receive related services under Section 504 even if they are not provided any special education. These are to be provided at no additional cost to the child and his or her parents. Section 504 requires provision of educational and related aids and services that are designed to meet the individual educational needs of the child. The individualized educational program of IDEA may be used to meet the Section 504 requirement.

Funding To Implement Requirements?

No. State and local jurisdictions have responsibility. IDEA funds may not be used to serve children found eligible only under Section 504.

Procedural Safeguards/Due Process

Section 504 requires notice to parents regarding identification, evaluation, placement, and before a "significant change" in placement. Written notice is recommended. Following IDEA procedural safeguards is one way to meet Section 504 mandates. Local education agencies are required to provide impartial hearings for parents who disagree with the identification, evaluation, or placement of a student. Parents must have an opportunity to participate in the hearing process and to be represented by counsel. Beyond this, due process is left to the discretion of local districts. It is recommended that they develop policy guidance and procedures.

Evaluation/Placement Procedures

Section 504 provides for a placement evaluation that must involve multiple assessment tools tailored to assess specific areas of educational need. Placement decisions must be made by a team of persons familiar with the student who understand the evaluation information and placement options. Students with disabilities may be placed in a separate class or facility only if they cannot be educated satisfactorily in the regular education setting with the use of supplementary aids and services. Significant changes to placement must be preceded by an evaluation.

Section 504 provides for periodic reevaluation. Parental consent is not required for evaluation or placement.

(References: See ERIC Digest E606)

Chapter 4

Changes in American Society

Name_____

CLASS REFLECTIONS - American Society

....

Date:_____   Topic:_____

Description:

_____

_____

_____

_____

_____

Analysis:

_____

_____

_____

_____

_____

Future Impact:

_____

_____

_____

_____

_____

_____

Date:_____   Topic:_____

Description:

_____

_____

_____

_____

Analysis:

_____

_____

_____

_____

Future Impact:

_____

_____

_____

_____

_____

Activity 4.1 - Review for Chapter 4

I. Clearly explain or define the following terms, concepts, or acronyms.

• latchkey children:

• middle class:

• poverty:

• resilient students:

• socioeconomic status:

• students placed at-risk:

• upper class:

• zero-tolerance programs:

II. What are the three major areas where changes are taking place in American society?

    1.

    2.

    3.

III. Research shows that less than 9% of America's poor live in the inner city. Why do most people think that the inner city is the home of America's poor?

IV. Identify five key areas of concern regarding the changing student population.

    1.

    2.

    3.

    4.

    5.

Activity 4.2 - School Reform and Safer Schools

Directions:
1. Read pages 122 & 123 in the text.
2. Check the topic you have been assigned.
   _____ Schoolwide Security Programs
   _____ Zero-Tolerance Programs
   _____ School Uniforms
3. Drawing on your experiences in, and knowledge of, other schools, identify four (4) strategies that could be used to address your assigned topic.
4. List the positives and negatives for each strategy.

STRATEGY	POSITIVES	NEGATIVES
1.		
2.		

STRATEGY	POSITIVES	NEGATIVES
3.		
4.		

Name_____

Activity 4.3 - Contemporary Concerns for Today's Teachers

In one to two sentences each, identify and describe seven (7) student-related concerns for today's teachers. All of them must be for the same grade range. Check the range you are addressing:

_____Elementary School   _____Middle School   _____High School.

1.

2.

3.

4.

5.

6.

7.

60

Resource 4.1

Profiling Students for Violence
Linda Lumsden
(ERIC Digest ED446344)

In the aftermath of the flurry of shootings and other incidents of violence that have erupted in our nation's schools during the past few years, teachers and administrators are desperately seeking reliable ways of foretelling which students may be at serious risk of crossing over the invisible line into violence. Although there is no crystal ball that can predict with certainty an individual student's future potential for violence, school officials are intensifying their efforts to identify potentially dangerous students.

Student profiling is one controversial approach to violence prevention that many administrators are contemplating in their quest to keep schools safe. While some perceive profiling as a promising tool, others view it as an ill-conceived response to the issue of school violence that will do more harm than good. This Digest defines profiling, discusses issues raised by profiling students for violence, and describes additional strategies for reducing the risk of violence in schools.

WHAT IS STUDENT PROFILING?

Student profiling is a term used to refer to a process in which checklists of behaviors and personal characteristics associated with youth who have perpetrated violence are used to try to gauge an individual student's potential for acting out in a violent manner in the future. If a large number of items on the list appear to be true for a particular student, the assumption is that the student is at higher risk for committing violence.

As Fey and others (2000) state, "In inductive profiling, the profiler looks for patterns in the available data and infers possible outcomes-in the case of schools, possible acts of violence committed by students who fit the pattern. The strategy is used to predict behavior and apprehend potential offenders before they commit a crime" [emphasis in original].

SHOULD SCHOOL PERSONNEL ATTEMPT TO PREDICT STUDENT BEHAVIOR?

One central issue surrounding the prospect of profiling students for violence is whether school personnel should attempt to make predictions about an individual student's propensity for future violence, a task that has been elusive even for trained mental-health professionals.

U.S. Education Secretary Richard W. Riley opposes use of behavioral profiling by schools to identify potentially violent students. Riley contends a better way to enhance school safety is for teachers and administrators to create a caring environment that promotes a sense of connection among students and between students and staff (Kenneth Cooper 2000). Riley also points out that research conducted at the University of Oregon's Institute on Violence and Destructive Behavior indicates that when schools promote compassion, discipline, and peaceful conflict resolution they can prevent 80 percent of violent behavior (Cooper).

Joe Morrison, school director at North Allegheny, one of Pittsburgh's largest suburban school districts, states, "This is a business we shouldn't even consider getting into" (McKay 1999). He believes students could be unfairly labeled and information placed in their school files could haunt them for the remainder of their educational careers (McKay).

The School Shooter: A Threat Assessment Perspective (O'Toole 2000), a report recently released by the FBI, provides a model for assessing the seriousness of threats and offering intervention. The report states that "at this time, there is no research that has identified traits and characteristics that can reliably distinguish school shooters from other students" and asserts that developing a profile "may sound like a reasonable preventive measure, but in practice trying to draw up a catalogue or 'checklist' of warning signs to detect a potential school shooter can be shortsighted, even dangerous."

However, Mary Leiker, superintendent of the Kentwood, Michigan, Public Schools, which has implemented a program to assess students for violence, has a different perspective. She notes, "Profiling isn't something most of us think we're going to do. But.... the fact is, I have to live with myself. If I, as a superintendent and educator, left one stone unturned in trying to keep children safe, if I lost one child because of it, I don't know how I would cope" (LaFee 2000).

Many of those in support of profiling students for violence are convinced keeping schools safe is so critical that measures perceived as extreme are warranted. Some administrators are concerned that if violence visits their school they could confront legal action-as well as tremendous personal guilt-if they haven't done everything in their power to try to create a safe school environment. However, electing to engage in profiling also raises an array of legal and ethical issues for schools.

IS PROFILING RELIABLE?

A critical issue to be examined is whether profiling students for violence is a reliable process. That is, can profiling accurately predict a student's potential for perpetrating violence?

According to Lois Flaherty, a child and adolescent psychologist and spokesperson for the American Psychological Association, the verdict is still out.

62

She states, "I don't think we have any data to show whether it is effective or not. And the lack of research is just one of many issues here" (LaFee).

FBI agent Terry Royster argues that teachers, who observe and interact with students on a daily basis over time, are more reliable sources of information about which students are most troubled and in need of help. He says, "What I stress is to really forget the school shooter behavioral assessments and go into the classroom. Every teacher can tell you who's likely to cause trouble" (LaFee).

Another complicating factor is that there is not a single list of behavioral "warning signs" about which consensus exists among professionals. Rather, there are several lists, each developed by different educational and mental-health related organizations. When items on one list of "warning signs" are compared with items on another, there is often only low to moderate overlap (Fey and others).

In other words, even the issue of what variables may be indicators of future violence remains at least partially unresolved. Therefore, an initial challenge facing schools that opt to engage in student profiling is deciding which list of guidelines to use as the standard against which to assess youth.

Also, some warning-sign lists, like the one included in the Department of Education publication Early Warning, Timely Response (1998), were never intended to be used for profiling purposes. However, despite a strong caution to this effect contained within the publication itself, in some cases this message has gone unheeded, which disturbs Kevin Dwyer, one of the authors ("Profiling Students May Cause More Harm" 1999).

WHAT QUESTIONS AND CONCERNS ARE RAISED BY STUDENT PROFILING?

A decision about profiling should not be made lightly. Its implications for both students and schools are far-reaching and should be given due consideration.

One caveat is that although certain behavioral patterns or characteristics tend to be more prevalent among youth who commit violent acts, many youth may display these behaviors or characteristics-or fit the "profile"-yet never become violent. As LaFee states, "Descriptions of moody, angry, confrontational and low self-esteem can be used to describe almost any teenager at some point."

Fey and others also point out that "school authorities could face legal action, as well as negative media attention, once a student is wrongfully identified as being at risk for committing violence."

Another concern is expressed by Hill Walker, codirector of the Institute on Violence and Destructive Behavior at the University of Oregon, who notes that efforts to gauge students' propensity for future violence inevitably result in both false positives and false negatives ("Profiling Students May Cause More Harm"). Walker believes "the potential of abuse is as great as the potential of violence."

Other issues that remain unresolved are noted by Flattery: "There's the question of who is doing the identifying of students and the evaluation. What happens with the results? Will they be used to single kids out for further stigmatization and isolation? What are the civil liberties concerns?" (LaFee).

Fey and others underscore the fact that "stereotyping, discrimination, and the wrongful identification of potential perpetrators are ethically unjustified, even if the intention is to protect children from harm." As they also point out, implementing profiling alters a school's culture and climate, and "touches at the very core of what schools should and will look like" (Fey and others).

Another significant issue, raised by Pam Riley, executive director of the Center for the Prevention of School Violence, is that even if school personnel are able to accurately identify troubled students through profiling, most don't know what to do next (LaFee). Should school personnel just attempt to keep a close eye on the student? Can or should they require students/families to obtain mental health services? Move the student to an alternative educational placement? Expel the student?

WHAT OTHER OPTIONS CAN SCHOOLS EMPLOY TO PREVENT VIOLENCE?

Youth violence is an extremely complex issue, and it will take a concerted effort by many sectors of society to make headway in addressing the problem. Fortunately, some promising paths to pursue are at hand.

Elias and colleagues contend that schools can play a major role in preventing violence by choosing to invest in social and emotional learning as well as academic learning. They believe the mission of schools must include teaching students "to engage in thoughtful decision making, understand signs of one's own and others' feelings, listen accurately, remember what we hear and learn, communicate effectively, [and] respect differences." Assisting students to develop competence in such social and emotional skills will not only reduce interpersonal violence but will also foster a caring and cooperative environment that supports academic learning.

Engaging in what is sometimes referred to as incident profiling (as opposed to student profiling) can also aid schools in their quest to reduce violence and other behavioral incidents (LaFee). Incident profiling entails reviewing office-referral data to learn such things as the primary reasons students are sent to the office or suspended, locations in the school building where problems tend to occur (such as lunch room, hallways), whether incidents are clustered around certain segments of the school day, and so forth. Office-referral data are maintained by most schools but rarely reviewed and analyzed. The data can often reveal trends and shed light on adjustments that are needed in the school setting (for example, placing more teachers in the hallways to better monitor the between-class transition time if most incidents in a particular school are happening during these periods).

Functional assessments are another tool schools can use to address problem behavior at an individual level rather than a schoolwide level. In a functional assessment, data concerning factors that may be influencing a particular student's problematic behavior are collected through direct observation. The purpose of the assessment is to identify variables that trigger the behavior and factors that help to maintain it, form hypotheses about the purpose the behavior is serving for the individual, and ultimately to formulate a behavior-support plan to teach and promote desired behaviors to replace the problem behavior (Sprague and others 1998).

Michael Greene, executive director of The Violence Institute, says, "First and foremost school officials, whether administrators or teachers or whoever, have to listen to students in a non-judgmental manner. Often, that's all a child needs-someone to talk to. And that requires only minimal training" (LaFee).

In a time when communities across the country are clamoring for evidence that school leaders are doing everything in their power to prevent further episodes of school violence, administrators must carefully consider the potential risks as well as the possible benefits associated with anything being touted as a tool to make schools safer.

(References: See ERIC Digest ED446344)

Chapter 5

Educational Philosophy

Name_____

CLASS REFLECTIONS - Educational Philosophy

....

Date:_____   Topic:_____

Description:

_____

_____

_____

_____

_____

Analysis:

_____

_____

_____

_____

_____

Future Impact:

_____

_____

_____

_____

_____

_____

Date:_____ Topic:_____

Description:

_____

_____

_____

_____

_____

Analysis:

_____

_____

_____

_____

_____

_____

Future Impact:

_____

_____

_____

_____

_____

_____

Activity 5.1 - Review for Chapter 5

I. Describe each of the following educational philosophies.

- Essentialism:

- Perennialism:

- Postmodernism:

- Progressivism:

II. If you were required to select one, and only one, of the educational philosophies discussed in Chapter 5 (Essentialism, Perennialism, Postmodernism, and Progressivism) as your philosophy, which one would you choose? Explain why?

Philosophical choice_____

Rationale:

Name_____

Activity 5.2 - Toward A Philosophy of Education

The purpose of this activity is to assist you in developing your own philosophy of education. To assess your developing philosophy of education, respond to the following statements. Use this scale:

1 = Strongly Disagree   2 = Disagree   3 = Neither Agree nor Disagree
4 = Agree   5 = Strongly Agree

1. Schools should emphasize important knowledge more than students' personal interests.   1 2 3 4 5

2. Teachers should emphasize interdisciplinary subject matter that encourages project-oriented, democratic classrooms.   1 2 3 4 5

3. Schools should emphasize the search for personal meaning more than a fixed body of subject matter.   1 2 3 4 5

4. The primary aim of education is to develop a person's intellectual capacity.   1 2 3 4 5

5. Schools should emphasize the basic skills more than humanistic ideals.   1 2 3 4 5

6. Teachers should guide student learning rather than lecture and disseminate information.   1 2 3 4 5

7. The best teachers encourage personal responses and develop critical awareness in their students.   1 2 3 4 5

8. The goals of education should be similar for everyone; all students should understand the importance of literature, mathematics, and science of Western civilization.   1 2 3 4 5

9. The purpose of schools is to ensure practical preparation for life and work more than personal development.   1 2 3 4 5

10. Curriculum should emerge from students' needs and interests; it should not be prescribed in advance.　　1　2　3　4　5

11. The best education emphasizes the great works in the arts and humanities.　　1　2　3　4　5

12. It is more important for teachers to involve students in activities that analyze and criticize society than to accumulate a lot of information.　　1　2　3　4　5

13. Education should emphasize personal growth through problem solving in the present more than emphasizing preparation for a distant future.　　1　2　3　4　5

14. Human nature's most distinctive quality is the ability to reason; therefore, the intellect should be the focus of education.　　1　2　3　4　5

15. Schools often perpetuate racism and sexism that is camouflaged as traditional value.　　1　2　3　4　5

16. Teachers should help students learn a common core of knowledge, not experiment with their own views about curricula.　　1　2　3　4　5

Record your responses in the appropriate boxes and record the totals:

Perennialism:

Item # 4_____ + #8_____ + #11_____ + #14_____　=_____

Progressivism:

Item # 2_____ + #6_____ + #10_____ + #13_____　=_____

Essentialism:

Item # 1_____ + #5_____ + #9_____ + #16_____　=_____

Postmodernism:

Item # 3_____ + #7_____ + #12_____ + #15_____　=_____

Name_____

Activity 5.3 - My "Educational Philosophy" Worksheet

1. What I believe about the role of **Education** in society:

2. What I believe about the role of **Schools** in society:

3. What I believe about the role of **Teachers** in society:

4. What I believe about the role of **Students** in society:

Resource 5.1

My Pedagogic Creed
by John Dewey

John Dewey is considered by many educators to have been the most influential thinker on education in the twentieth century. Although his writings have addressed many aspects of education, his attention to experience and reflection, democracy and community, and to environments for learning have been especially significant. "My Pedagogic Creed," John Dewey's famous declaration concerning education, was first published in *The School Journal*, Volume LIV, Number 3 (January 16, 1897), pages 77-80.

ARTICLE I--What Education Is

I believe that all education proceeds by the participation of the individual in the social consciousness of the race. This process begins unconsciously almost at birth, and is continually shaping the individual's powers, saturating his consciousness, forming his habits, training his ideas, and arousing his feelings and emotions. Through this unconscious education the individual gradually comes to share in the intellectual and moral resources which humanity has succeeded in getting together. He becomes an inheritor of the funded capital of civilization. The most formal and technical education in the world cannot safely depart from this general process. It can only organize it or differentiate it in some particular direction.

I believe that the only true education comes through the stimulation of the child's powers by the demands of the social situations in which he finds himself. Through these demands he is stimulated to act as a member of a unity, to emerge from his original narrowness of action and feeling, and to conceive of himself from the standpoint of the welfare of the group to which he belongs. Through the responses which others make to his own activities he comes to know what these mean in social terms. The value which they have is reflected back into them. For instance, through the response which is made to the child's instinctive babblings the child comes to know what those babblings mean; they are transformed into articulate language and thus the child is introduced into the consolidated wealth of ideas and emotions which are now summed up in language.

I believe that this educational process has two sides-one psychological and one sociological; and that neither can be subordinated to the other or neglected without evil results following. Of these two sides, the psychological is the basis. The child's own instincts and powers furnish the material and give the starting point for all education. Save as the efforts of the educator connect with some activity which the child is carrying on of his own initiative independent of the educator, education becomes reduced to a pressure from without. It may, indeed, give certain external results, but cannot truly be called educative. Without insight into the psychological structure and activities of the individual, the educative process will, therefore, be haphazard and arbitrary. If it chances to coincide with the child's activity it will get a leverage; if it does not, it will result in friction, or disintegration, or arrest of the child nature.

I believe that knowledge of social conditions, of the present state of civilization, is necessary in order properly to interpret the child's powers. The child has his own instincts and tendencies, but we do not know what these mean until we can translate them into their social equivalents. We must be able to carry them back into a social past and see them as the inheritance of previous race activities. We must also be able to project them into the future to see what their outcome and end will be. In the illustration just used, it is the ability to see in the child's babblings the promise and potency of a future social intercourse and conversation which enables one to deal in the proper way with that instinct.

I believe that the psychological and social sides are organically related and that education cannot be regarded as a compromise between the two, or a superimposition of one upon the other. We are told that the psychological definition of education is barren and formal--that it gives us only the idea of a development of all the mental powers without giving us any idea of the use to which these powers are put. On the other hand, it is urged that the social definition of education, as getting adjusted to civilization, makes of it a forced and external process, and results in subordinating the freedom of the individual to a preconceived social and political status.

I believe that each of these objections is true when urged against one side isolated from the other. In order to know what a power really is we must know what its end, use, or function is; and this we cannot know save as we conceive of the individual as active in social relationships. But, on the other hand, the only possible adjustment which we can give to the child under existing conditions, is that which arises through putting him in complete possession of all his powers. With the advent of democracy and modern industrial conditions, it is impossible to foretell definitely just what civilization will be twenty years from now. Hence it is impossible to prepare the child for any precise set of conditions. To prepare him for the future life means to give him command of himself; it means so to train him that he will have the full and ready use of all his capacities; that his eye and ear and hand may be tools ready to command, that his judgment may be capable of grasping the conditions under which it has to work, and the executive forces be trained to act economically and efficiently. It is impossible to reach this sort of adjustment save as constant regard is had to the individual's own powers, tastes, and interests-say, that is, as education is continually converted into psychological terms.

In sum, I believe that the individual who is to be educated is a social individual and that society is an organic union of individuals. If we eliminate the social factor from the child we are left only with an abstraction; if we eliminate the individual factor from society, we are left only with an inert and lifeless mass. Education, therefore, must begin with a psychological insight into the child's capacities, interests, and habits. It must be controlled at every point by reference to these same considerations. These powers, interests, and habits must be continually interpreted--we must know what they mean. They must be translated into terms of their social equivalents--into terms of what they are capable of in the way of social service.

ARTICLE II--What the School Is

I believe that the school is primarily a social institution. Education being a social process, the school is simply that form of community life in which all those agencies are concentrated that will be most effective in bringing the child to share in the inherited resources of the race, and to use his own powers for social ends.

I believe that education, therefore, is a process of living and not a preparation for future living.

I believe that the school must represent present life-life as real and vital to the child as that which he carries on in the home, in the neighborhood, or on the playground.

I believe that education which does not occur through forms of life, or that are worth living for their own sake, is always a poor substitute for the genuine reality and tends to cramp and to deaden.

I believe that the school, as an institution, should simplify existing social life; should reduce it, as it were, to an embryonic form. Existing life is so complex that the child cannot be brought into contact with it without either confusion or distraction; he is either overwhelmed by the multiplicity of activities which are going on, so that he loses his own power of orderly reaction, or he is so stimulated by these various activities that his powers are prematurely called into play and he becomes either unduly specialized or else disintegrated.

I believe that as such simplified social life, the school life should grow gradually out of the home life; that it should take up and continue the activities with which the child is already familiar in the home.

I believe that it should exhibit these activities to the child, and reproduce them in such ways that the child will gradually learn the meaning of them, and be capable of playing his own part in relation to them.

I believe that this is a psychological necessity, because it is the only way of securing continuity in the child's growth, the only way of giving a back-ground of past experience to the new ideas given in school.

I believe that it is also a social necessity because the home is the form of social life in which the child has been nurtured and in connection with which he has had his moral training. It is the business of the school to deepen and extend his sense of the values bound up in his home life.

I believe that much of present education fails because it neglects this fundamental principle of the school as a form of community life. It conceives the school as a place where certain information is to be given, where certain lessons are to be]earned, or where certain habits are to be formed. The value of these is conceived as lying largely in the remote future; the child must do these things for the sake of something else he is to do; they are mere preparation. As a result they do not become a part of the life experience of the child and so are not truly educative.

I believe that the moral education centers upon this conception of the school as a mode of social life, that the best and deepest moral training is precisely that which one gets through having to enter into proper relations with others in a unity of work and thought. The present educational systems, so far as they destroy or neglect this unity, render it difficult or impossible to get any genuine, regular moral training.

I believe that the child should be stimulated and controlled in his work through the life of the community.

I believe that under existing conditions far too much of the stimulus and control proceeds from the teacher, because of neglect of the idea of the school as a form of social life.

I believe that the teacher's place and work in the school is to be interpreted from this same basis. The teacher is not in the school to impose certain ideas or to form certain habits in the child, but is there as a member of the community to select the influences which shall affect the child and to assist him in properly responding to these influences.

I believe that the discipline of the school should proceed from the life of the school as a whole and not directly from the teacher.

I believe that the teacher's business is simply to determine on the basis of larger experience and riper wisdom, how the discipline of life shall come to the child.

I believe that all questions of the grading of the child and his promotion should be determined by reference to the same standard. Examinations are of use only so far as they test the child's fitness for social life and reveal the place in which he can be of the most service and where he can receive the most help.

ARTICLE III--The Subject-Matter of Education

I believe that the social life of the child is the basis of concentration, or correlation, in all his training or growth. The social life gives the unconscious unity and the background of all his efforts and of all his attainments.

I believe that the subject-matter of the school curriculum should mark a gradual differentiation out of the primitive unconscious unity of social life.

I believe that we violate the child's nature and render difficult the best ethical results, by introducing the child too abruptly to a number of special studies, of reading, writing, geography, etc., out of relation to this social life.

I believe, therefore, that the true center of correlation on the school subjects is not science, nor literature, nor history, nor geography, but the child's own social activities.

I believe that education cannot be unified in the study of science, or so called nature study, because apart from human activity, nature itself is not a unity; nature in itself is a number of diverse objects in space and time, and to attempt to make it the center of work by itself, is to introduce a principle of radiation rather than one of concentration.

I believe that literature is the reflex expression and interpretation of social experience; that hence it must follow upon and not precede such experience. It, therefore, cannot be made the basis, although it may be made the summary of unification.

I believe once more that history is of educative value in so far as it presents phases of social life and growth. It must be controlled by reference to social life. When taken simply as history it is thrown into the distant past and becomes dead and inert. Taken as the record of man's social life and progress it becomes full of meaning. I believe, however, that it cannot be so taken excepting as the child is also introduced directly into social life.

I believe accordingly that the primary basis of education is in the child's powers at work along the same general constructive lines as those which have brought civilization into being.

I believe that the only way to make the child conscious of his social heritage is to enable him to perform those fundamental types of activity which make civilization what it is.

I believe, therefore, in the so-called expressive or constructive activities as the center of correlation.

I believe that this gives the standard for the place of cooking, sewing, manual training, etc., in the school.

I believe that they are not special studies which are to be introduced over and above a lot of others in the way of relaxation or relief, or as additional accomplishments. I believe rather that they represent, as types, fundamental forms of social activity; and that it is possible and desirable that the child's introduction into the more formal subjects of the curriculum be through the medium of these activities.

I believe that the study of science is educational in so far as it brings out the materials and processes which make social life what it is.

I believe that one of the greatest difficulties in the present teaching of science is that the material is presented in purely objective form, or is treated as a new peculiar kind of experience which the child can add to that which he has already had. In reality, science is of value because it gives the ability to interpret and control the experience already had. It should be introduced, not as so much new subject-matter, but as showing the factors already involved in previous experience and as furnishing tools by which that experience can be more easily and effectively regulated.

I believe that at present we lose much of the value of literature and language studies because of our elimination of the social element. Language is almost always treated in the books of pedagogy simply as the expression of thought. It is true that language is a logical instrument, but it is fundamentally and primarily a social instrument. Language is the device for communication; it is the tool through which one individual comes to share the ideas and feelings of others. When treated simply as a way of getting individual information, or as a means of showing off what one has learned, it loses its social motive and end.

I believe that there is, therefore, no succession of studies in the ideal school curriculum. If education is life, all life has, from the outset, a scientific aspect, an aspect of art and culture, and an aspect of communication. It cannot, therefore, be true that the proper studies for one grade are mere reading and writing, and that at a later grade, reading, or literature, or science, may be introduced. The progress is not in the succession of studies but in the development of new attitudes towards, and new interests in, experience.

I believe finally, that education must be conceived as a continuing reconstruction of experience; that the process and the goal of education are one and the same thing.

I believe that to set up any end outside of education, as furnishing its goal and standard, is to deprive the educational process of much of its meaning and tends to make us rely upon false and external stimuli in dealing with the child.

ARTICLE IV--The Nature of Method

I believe that the question of method is ultimately reducible to the question of the order of development of the child's powers and interests. The law for presenting and treating material is the law implicit within the child's own nature. Because this is so I believe the following statements are of supreme importance as determining the spirit in which education is carried on:

1. I believe that the active side precedes the passive in the development of the child nature; that expression comes before conscious impression; that the muscular development precedes the sensory; that movements come before conscious sensations; I believe that consciousness is essentially motor or impulsive; that conscious states tend to project themselves in action.

I believe that the neglect of this principle is the cause of a large part of the waste of time and strength in school work. The child is thrown into a passive, receptive, or absorbing attitude. The conditions are such that he is not permitted to follow the law of his nature; the result is friction and waste.

I believe that ideas (intellectual and rational processes) also result from action and devolve for the sake of the better control of action. What we term reason is primarily the law of orderly or effective action. To attempt to develop the reasoning powers, the powers of judgment, without reference to the selection and arrangement of means in action, is the fundamental fallacy in our present methods of dealing with this matter. As a result we present the child with arbitrary symbols. Symbols are a necessity in mental development, but they have their place as tools for economizing effort; presented by themselves they are a mass of meaningless and arbitrary ideas imposed from without.

2. I believe that the image is the great instrument of instruction. What a child gets out of any subject presented to him is simply the images which he himself forms with regard to it.

I believe that if nine tenths of the energy at present directed towards making the child learn certain things, were spent in seeing to it that the child was forming proper images, the work of instruction would be indefinitely facilitated.

I believe that much of the time and attention now given to the preparation and presentation of lessons might be more wisely and profitably expended in training the child's power of imagery and in seeing to it that he was continually forming definite, vivid, and growing images of the various subjects with which he comes in contact in his experience.

3. I believe that interests are the signs and symptoms of growing power. I believe that they represent dawning capacities. Accordingly the constant and careful observation of interests is of the utmost importance for the educator.

I believe that these interests are to be observed as showing the state of development which the child has reached.

I believe that they prophesy the stage upon which he is about to enter.

I believe that only through the continual and sympathetic observation of childhood's interests can the adult enter into the child's life and see what it is ready for, and upon what material it could work most readily and fruitfully.

I believe that these interests are neither to be humored nor repressed. To repress interest is to substitute the adult for the child, and so to weaken intellectual curiosity and alertness, to suppress initiative, and to deaden interest. To humor the interests is to substitute the transient for the permanent. The interest is always the sign of some power below; the important thing is to discover this power. To humor the interest is to fail to penetrate below the surface and its sure result is to substitute caprice and whim for genuine interest.

4. I believe that the emotions are the reflex of actions.

I believe that to endeavor to stimulate or arouse the emotions apart from their corresponding activities, is to introduce an unhealthy and morbid state of mind.

I believe that if we can only secure right habits of action and thought, with reference to the good, the true, and the beautiful, the emotions will for the most part take care of themselves.

I believe that next to deadness and dullness, formalism and routine, our education is threatened with no greater evil than sentimentalism.

I believe that this sentimentalism is the necessary result of the attempt to divorce feeling from action.

ARTICLE V-The School and Social Progress

I believe that education is the fundamental method of social progress and reform.

I believe that all reforms which rest simply upon the enactment of law, or the threatening of certain penalties, or upon changes in mechanical or outward arrangements, are transitory and futile.

I believe that education is a regulation of the process of coming to share in the social consciousness; and that the adjustment of individual activity on the basis of this social consciousness is the only sure method of social reconstruction.

I believe that this conception has due regard for both the individualistic and socialistic ideals. It is duly individual because it recognizes the formation of a certain character as the only genuine basis of right living. It is socialistic because it recognizes that this right character is not to be formed by merely individual precept, example, or exhortation, but rather by the influence of a certain form of institutional or community life upon the individual, and that the social organism through the school, as its organ, may determine ethical results.

I believe that in the ideal school we have the reconciliation of the individualistic and the institutional ideals.

I believe that the community's duty to education is, therefore, its paramount moral duty. By law and punishment, by social agitation and discussion, society can regulate and form itself in a more or less haphazard and chance way. But through education society can formulate its own purposes, can organize its own means and resources, and thus shape itself with definiteness and economy in the direction in which it wishes to move.

I believe that when society once recognizes the possibilities in this direction, and the obligations which these possibilities impose, it is impossible to conceive of the resources of time, attention, and money which will be put at the disposal of the educator.

I believe that it is the business of every one interested in education to insist upon the school as the primary and most effective interest of social progress and reform in order that society may be awakened to realize what the school stands for, and aroused to the necessity of endowing the educator with sufficient equipment properly to perform his task.

I believe that education thus conceived marks the most perfect and intimate union of science and art conceivable in human experience.

I believe that the art of thus giving shape to human powers and adapting them to social service, is the supreme art; one calling into its service the best of artists; that no insight, sympathy, tact, executive power, is too great for such service.

I believe that with the growth of psychological service, giving added insight into individual structure and laws of growth; and with growth of social science, adding to our knowledge of the right organization of individuals, all scientific resources can be utilized for the purposes of education.

I believe that when science and art thus join hands the most commanding motive for human action will be reached; the most genuine springs of human conduct aroused and the best service that human nature is capable of guaranteed.

I believe, finally, that the teacher is engaged, not simply in the training of individuals, but in the formation of the proper social life.

I believe that every teacher should realize the dignity of his calling; that he is a social servant set apart for the maintenance of proper social order and the securing of the right social growth.

Chapter 6

The Organization of American Schools

Name_____

CLASS REFLECTIONS - American Schools

....

Date:_____   Topic:_____

Description:

_____

_____

_____

_____

_____

Analysis:

_____

_____

_____

_____

_____

Future Impact:

_____

_____

_____

_____

_____

_____

Date:_____   Topic:_____

Description:

_____

_____

_____

_____

_____

Analysis:

_____

_____

_____

_____

_____

Future Impact:

_____

_____

_____

_____

_____

Name_____

Activity 6.1 - Review for Chapter 6

I. Clearly explain or define the following terms, concepts, or acronyms.

- advanced placement classes:

- curriculum:

- curriculum specialist:

- developmental programs:

- early-childhood education:

- effective school:

- middle school:

- personal teaching efficacy:

• school district:

• support staff:

II. Identify and discuss the two main criticisms of the Comprehensive High School.

1.

2.

II. Identify three benefits of parental involvement in a student's education.

1.

2.

3.

Name_____

Activity 6.2
Was The High School You Attended An Effective School?

Directions: Describe the high school you attended regarding the following
characteristics.

Estimated Total Student Population:

Typical Class Size:

School Safety, Discipline, and Order:

Academic Focus Set Forth by Teachers, Counselors, and the Administration:

Parental/Guardian Involvement in the School:

General Attitude of the Teachers:

Overall Quality of the Instruction:

The Ways Student Progress Was Monitored:

Resource 6.1

New Jersey Charter Schools Fact Sheet

A charter school is a public school operated under a charter granted by the Commissioner of Education, that is independent of the district board of education and that is managed by a board of trustees.

Charter school legislation was passed to give choice for all parents for their children's education. The intent of this legislation is to:

- Improve student learning and achievement;
- Increase the availability of choice to parents and students when selecting a learning environment;
- Encourage the use of different and innovative learning methods;
- Establish a new system of accountability for schools;
- Make the school the unit for educational improvement;
- Establish new professional opportunities for teachers.

Founders of a charter school may be teaching staff members, parents with children attending schools of the district or a combination of both, as well as institutions of higher education or a private entity located within the State in conjunction with teaching staff members and parents.

Charter schools may not charge tuition.

A private or parochial school may not convert to a charter school.

A charter school is open to all students on a space-available basis with preference being given to students from the district of residence or region of residence of the charter school.

All classroom teachers and professional support staff must hold appropriate New Jersey certification.

CURRENT STATISTICS

As of January 2005, there are 55 approved charter schools in New Jersey. Forty-nine are operating and three are scheduled to open in September 2005;

In September 2004, Princeton Charter School became the first charter school in New Jersey to achieve National Blue Ribbon School of Excellence status;

As of September 2004, New Jersey's charter schools are serving over 14,000 students in pre-kindergarten through grade 12;

Fourteen counties have approved charter schools;

All of New Jersey's charter schools are newly created. There are no charter schools that have been converted from other public schools;

The average enrollment in a charter school is 193 students;

The average class size of charter schools is 17 students;

The average school year for charter schools is 186 days;

The average length of the school day in charter schools is slightly over 7 hours; students are engaged in instruction for an average of slightly over 6 hours;

In 2004, four of the charter schools that opened in September 2000 were granted charter renewals for an additional five-year period.

Resource 6.2

Schools Within Schools
Tobin McAndrews & Wendell Anderson
(ERIC Digest 461915)

Growing numbers of educators and parents across the nation are drawn to the idea of downsizing schools. Numerous studies and successful model programs have confirmed the academic, social, and financial benefits of small-scale schooling.

Most discussions of small schools focus on which model to choose and how best to implement the downsizing. One model that is gaining increasing favor is "schools within schools." The advantages, drawbacks, varieties, and sources of funding for schools within schools are discussed in this Digest.

WHAT ARE SCHOOLS WITHIN SCHOOLS?

Schools within schools are large public schools that have been divided into smaller autonomous subunits. The National Association of Elementary School Principals officially recognizes a school within a school as "a separate entity, running its own budget and planning its own programs. However, school safety and building operation remain vested with the principal of the larger school, and use of shared space must be negotiated" (NAESP).

Designers of schools within schools seek the advantages of both large and small schools by placing students into small learning communities while using the resources of the larger existing facilities. Those resources include faculty and staff. "Small school," a type of school within a school, employs faculty and staff brought in from elsewhere in the district rather than from the larger school (NAESP).

A key organizational characteristic of the school within a school is that the program and individual classes remain small (Sicoli 2000). Researchers and reformers have identified the optimum number of students in a program to be as many as 500 and as few as 30. A number of factors, including reasons for the program and the size of the school in which the program will be housed, determine optimum size (Sicoli).

WHAT ARE SOME OF THE BENEFITS OF SMALL SCHOOLS?

Although few studies have been conducted on the school-within-a-school model itself, proponents infer that the benefits of a school within a school closely parallel those found in small schools, which have been widely investigated.

In 1996, a report from the National Association of Secondary School Principals and the Carnegie Foundation for the Advancement of Teaching recommended smaller schools and smaller classes as essential for student improvement. Research shows that smaller learning environments create happier, safer, higher achieving students (Oxley 2001).

Summarized here are some of the advantages of small schools identified by researchers. Depending on physical layout and resources, the advantages of small schools can apply to schools within schools.

Academic benefits: Test scores of students in small schools are consistently higher than those in larger schools (McComb 2000; Jacobson, February 28, 2001). Administrators of small schools are also better able to reform their curricula and teaching strategies (McComb). Smaller class sizes and interdisciplinary methods allow greater contact between student and teacher. And because teachers in smaller schools tend to be more aware of student performance, student accountability is increased.

Social benefits: The greater sense of belonging that students feel in small schools fosters more caring through interpersonal relationships (Capps 1999). Small-school settings have been shown to enhance students' self- perceptions, both socially and academically (McPartland). Small schools also foster a more aware and involved faculty, which promotes positive student attitudes (McPartland). Additionally, in small schools there is more opportunity for student involvement in school activities because of less competition for membership on athletic teams and in clubs and student government (McComb).

Attendance and graduation benefits: The average national dropout rate for high schools with more than 1,000 students is 6.39 percent, whereas schools with fewer than 200 students have an average dropout rate of 3.47 percent (McComb). Research shows that small schools have higher rates of attendance than large schools have (Gewertz 2001). These variations may be due to the relative ease of staff members at the small-school level to recognize students and hold them accountable.

Safety and discipline benefits: Small schools generally have fewer discipline problems than larger schools. The strong parental support and adult connections often present in small schools create a safer environment for students. Strangers can be spotted more easily in small schools, which further promotes safety (McComb).

Financial benefits: Studies have shown that larger schools spend more per student as administrative costs grow with larger student bodies. Also, the cost of "learning per unit" is higher in larger schools as a result of their often less favorable academic outcomes (Lawton). A study in 1998 in New York City found that small schools were more cost effective because more of their students graduated on time (Gewertz).

WHAT ARE SOME DRAWBACKS OF SMALL SCHOOLS?

Support for small schools, however, is not unconditional. "Small, in and of itself, can be as silly as big," said Michelle Fine, a professor of psychology at the City University of New York (in Gewertz). "It will produce a sense of belonging almost immediately. But hugging is not the same as algebra. Rigor and care must be braided together, or we run the risk of creating small, nurturing environments that aren't schools" (Fine in Gewertz).

Several staffing issues arise when large schools are carved into smaller units. Some teachers worry that they may have to transfer from one school to another, may lose seniority in doing so, may have to teach out of their specialty in a school with fewer course offerings, or may not truly gain the autonomy they desire in the downsizing of schools (Gewertz).

A survey by Public Agenda showed that parents and teachers chose reducing class size and improving discipline over making schools smaller as ways to improve the educational experience. A majority of teachers surveyed believed that smaller schools will have less money for equipment and that it will be more difficult for students who have problems with teachers to transfer out of classes (Jacobson, October 3, 2001).

To avoid segregation along racial, ethnic, and socioeconomic lines, care must be taken when assigning students to smaller learning communities.

WHAT ARE SOME TYPES OF SCHOOLS WITHIN SCHOOLS?

School-within-school plans were initially conceived to offer alternatives to parents who wanted a specialized education for their children not available through the normal school structure or standard curriculum. Administrators have devised a variety of plans in accordance with the special circumstances and resources of their districts. Nine such plans have become common.

Vertical-house plans: First instituted in the United Kingdom, these plans serve students in grades 9 through 12 or 10 through 12. Typically a school of 1,000 or more students is broken up into groups of several hundred students. Each "house" shares the same faculty and facilities but has autonomous policies for student discipline, activities, government, and parental involvement.

Ninth-grade house plans: These plans are similar to the vertical-house model but involve only the ninth grade (Cawelti 1993, Oxley).

At-risk schools: These plans serve students who have not responded well to traditional learning environments. A typical model includes traditional academic curriculum along with an academy program in which students learn a trade such as computer repair.

Career academies and clusters: In these models students engage in classes or house systems aligned with their interests and possible career choices.

Special-curriculum models: These schools offer advanced courses for high-achieving students. Students are divided into houses based on their special needs or interests (Cawelti).

Newcomer schools: Newcomer schools are sometimes established in areas where a large number of students-generally elementary school students-are entering a school system for the first time and having difficulty with the transition (Boloz and Blessing 1994).

Parent-participation plans: In these plans parents of elementary-school children are permitted to enroll their children in the school only after making a commitment to donate a specific amount of their time and energy as teachers.

Advisory systems: Under these systems students are placed under the guidance and care of either a teacher or administrator for their entire school experience. In effect, the student acquires a personal academic and social guidance counselor.

Charter schools: Similar to special-curriculum schools, charter schools develop curricula independent of the public system. Charter schools are generally developed by parents or teachers seeking an alternative to standard programs. Charter schools, nevertheless, are held to the same standards of educational achievement as public schools.

HOW DO ADMINISTRATORS DEVELOP AND FUND A SCHOOL WITHIN A SCHOOL?

Developing a school within a school requires careful planning. Administrators must assess the need for and purpose of their plan before committing resources. Initial plans must include components for hiring faculty and staff, developing curriculum and admittance policies, and selecting facilities and equipment.

Additionally, administrators should decide the type and extent of possible subschooling systems to implement, such as programs in art, business, college prep, sciences, and community studies. The satisfaction of designing a school within a school is the nearly limitless possibilities. The scope of classes and programs that can be offered is only a matter of imagination coupled with resources.

In the nonprofit sector, the Annenberg Foundation, the Pew Charitable Trust, and the Bill and Melinda Gates Foundation have offered more than $1 billion for the planning and implementation of smaller learning communities. The Bill and Melinda Gates Foundation has pledged more than $240 million over the next several years to help districts downsize their schools (Jacobson, October 3, 2001).

(References: See ERIC Digest 461915)

Chapter 7

School Law

Name_____

CLASS REFLECTIONS - School Law

....

Date:_____   Topic:_____

Description:

_____

_____

_____

_____

_____

Analysis:

_____

_____

_____

_____

_____

_____

Future Impact:

_____

_____

_____

_____

_____

_____

Date:_____ Topic:_____

Description:

_____

_____

_____

_____

_____

Analysis:

_____

_____

_____

_____

_____

Future Impact:

_____

_____

_____

_____

_____

Name_____

Activity 7.1 - Review for Chapter 7

I. Clearly explain or define the following terms, concepts, or acronyms.

• academic freedom:

• Buckley Amendment:

• corporal punishment:

• *in loco parentis*:

• professional ethics:

• reduction in force:

II. What issues did the following court cases address?

1. Hazelwood School District v. Kuhlmeier

2. New Jersey v. T.L.O.

3. Tinker v. Des Moines Community School District

III. Identify three reasons a tenured teacher can be dismissed.

1.

2.

3.

IV. In 1997 the state of Oregon eliminated tenure for teachers and replaced it with two-year contracts. Identify three reasons to support this decision.

1.

2.

3.

Name_____

Activity 7.2
How Have Supreme Court Decisions Affected Public Schools?

For each of the following practices, check whether the Supreme Court has held that practice to be mandatory ("Must"), permitted ("May"), or prohibited ("Must Not").

	Must	May	Must Not
1. A school district___require...the posting in each classroom of a copy of the Ten Commandments which has been obtained via private contributions and which is expressly labeled as nonreligious material.			
2. A school district___provide classes to nonpublic school students in classrooms located in nonpublic schools.			
3. A school district___dismiss a teacher for expressing criticism of school policies or practices that are not of public interest.			
4. A school district___dismiss teachers who engage in an illegal strike unless the teachers can show the board's decision was based on personal, pecuniary, or antiunion bias.			
5. A school district___allow the union that is the exclusive bargaining agent sole access to its interschool mail system and teacher mailboxes, limiting access by rival unions and groups.			
6. A school district___permit nonexcessive corporal punishment of students under the authorization or in the absence of a state mandate.			
7. A school district___conduct a search of a student, without the assistance of police, if the school authorities have reasonable suspicion...that the student has violated or is violating the law or school rules.			
8. A school district___refuse to provide clean-intermittent-catheterization for handicapped students who need this service to attend school.			
9. A school district___deny enrollment in their public schools to children who are "illegal aliens" in the United states.			
10. A school district___discipline students for using lewd and offensive language that does not cause a substantial disruption in the school.			

Resource 7.1

Reporting Child Abuse in New Jersey
(in conformity with 18A:36-24 and 9:6-8)

In New Jersey, the Division of Youth and Family services (DYFS) investigates reports of suspected child abuse and neglect. DYFS staff are available to receive referrals at the local district office from 9:00 am to 5:00 pm and at the Office of Child Abuse Control (OCAC) at any hour (1-800-792-8610). Calls received at OCAC during normal working hours are immediately referred to the appropriate district office.

DYFS accepts all reports of suspected child abuse and neglect and other referrals in writing, by telephone, and in person from all sources including identified sources, news media, anonymous sources, sources which have incomplete information, and referrals from the child or parent him/herself.

TYPES OF ABUSE: Physical, Sexual, Emotional, Neglect, Abandonment

CLASSROOM SIGNS:

- Poor performance
- Frequent complaints of pain
- Malnourishment
- Ill-clothed/dirty

- Disruptive behaviors
- Withdrawn/quiet behavior
- Abnormal absences
- Lack of necessary medical attention

- Nervous habit
- Tiredness
- Physical injuries

You are immune from civil or criminal liability if you report suspected child abuse or neglect or testify in a child abuse hearing. You cannot be sued. (NJSA 9:6-8.13)

Failure to report suspected abuse or neglect makes you a disorderly person subject to a fine up to $500, up to six months in jail, or both. Failure to report also could result in a law suit if it is realized that a school employee had suspicion or knowledge of abuse or neglect and it was not reported.

Teachers and nurses do not have to substantiate their suspicions. They are only required to report them.

All school employees are required by law to report suspected abuse/neglect directly to DYFS. Notify the building principal or a designee (per board policy).

Every district should have a written policy on dealing with child abuse/neglect. This is required by law; be sure to get a copy.

You may choose not to give your identity when reporting.

DYFS tries to keep all reports confidential. DYFS can give the information to certain agencies, as directed by law.

It is suggested that you do not press children about injuries.

Do not contact the parents. As a teacher candidate, refer your concerns to your cooperating teacher, who will take appropriate action.

Resource 7.2

Corporal Punishment

New Jersey Statute 18A:6-1. Corporal punishment of pupils

No person employed or engaged in a school or educational institution, whether public or private, shall inflict or cause to be inflicted corporal punishment upon a pupil attending such school or institution; but any such person may, within the scope of his employment, use and apply such amounts of force as is reasonable and necessary:
>   (1) to quell a disturbance, threatening physical injury
>   to others;
>   (2) to obtain possession of weapons or other
>   dangerous objects upon the person or within the
>   control of a pupil;
>   (3) for the purpose of self-defense; and
>   (4) for the protection of persons or property;

and such acts, or any of them, shall not be construed to constitute corporal punishment within the meaning and intendment of this section. Every resolution, bylaw, rule, ordinance, or other act or authority permitting or authorizing corporal punishment to be inflicted upon a pupil attending a school or educational institution shall be void.

- Corporal punishment of pupils has been prohibited in New Jersey since 1867.

- In 1938 the Commissioner of Education defined corporal punishment as: "...any punishment causing or intending to cause bodily pain and suffering."

- In 1977 the U.S. Supreme Court (Ingraham v. Wright, 1977) ruled that states may constitutionally authorize corporal punishment without prior hearing or notice and without consent by the students' parents and may as a matter of policy elect to prohibit or limit the use of corporal punishment. They stated that the safeguards of the Eighth Amendment do not apply to school children.

- Where corporal punishment is allowed, the legality of the corporal punishment administered is determined by factors such as the severity of the punishment, the size and age of the pupil, instrument used, etc.

States that Forbid Corporal Punishment in Schools and Year of Decision

New Jersey – 1867

Massachusetts – 1971

Hawaii – 1873

Rhode Island – 1975

Maine – 1975

New Hampshire – 1975

Vermont – 1984

New York – 1985

California – 1987

Nebraska – 1988

Wisconsin – 1988

Michigan - 1988

Virginia - 1989

North Dakota - 1989

Oregon - 1989

Minnesota - 1989

Indiana - 1989

Connecticut - 1989

Alaska - 1989

South Dakota - 1990

Utah - 1992

Past Examples of Corporal Punishment

- A first grade student was given three swats with a paddle because she circled and did not underline a word in a reading lesson. (Ohio)

- Twenty-two grade school pupils were paddled because they did not bring their watercolors to art class. (Texas)

- An eleven-year-old girl was caught chewing gum in class. The teacher spanked her and allowed the entire class to come up and hit her on the buttocks with a paddle. (Michigan)

- Three sixth-graders who received scores below 80 on a math exam received paddling by their fellow classmates. The teacher said that those who scored above 80 would be rewarded with a day free of work if they punished the lowest scorers by paddling them. (Wyoming)

A Compelling Thought

Corporal punishment is outlawed in the military, in mental institutions and in prisons. The school is the sole institution in our society in which such punishment is still allowed, despite the complete lack of evidence that this "educational tool" does anything to enhance learning. In fact, continuing to allow corporal punishment in American classrooms flies directly in the face of current efforts to find and teach nonviolent methods of discipline.

Resource 7.3

The Family Educational Rights and Privacy Act (FERPA)
(The Buckley Amendment)

The Family Educational Rights and Privacy Act (FERPA) (20 U.S.C. § 1232g; 34 CFR Part 99) is a Federal law that protects the privacy of student education records. The law applies to all schools that receive funds under an applicable program of the U.S. Department of Education.

FERPA gives parents certain rights with respect to their children's education records. These rights transfer to the student when he or she reaches the age of 18 or attends a school beyond the high school level. Students to whom the rights have transferred are "eligible students."

Parents or eligible students have the right to inspect and review the student's education records maintained by the school. Schools are not required to provide copies of records unless, for reasons such as great distance, it is impossible for parents or eligible students to review the records. Schools may charge a fee for copies.

Parents or eligible students have the right to request that a school correct records which they believe to be inaccurate or misleading. If the school decides not to amend the record, the parent or eligible student then has the right to a formal hearing. After the hearing, if the school still decides not to amend the record, the parent or eligible student has the right to place a statement with the record setting forth his or her view about the contested information.

Generally, schools must have written permission from the parent or eligible student in order to release any information from a student's education record. However, FERPA allows schools to disclose those records, without consent, to the following parties or under the following conditions (34 CFR § 99.31):

- School officials with legitimate educational interest;
- Other schools to which a student is transferring;
- Specified officials for audit or evaluation purposes;
- Appropriate parties in connection with financial aid to a student;
- Organizations conducting certain studies for or on behalf of the school;
- Accrediting organizations;
- To comply with a judicial order or lawfully issued subpoena;
- Appropriate officials in cases of health and safety emergencies; and
- State and local authorities, within a juvenile justice system, pursuant to specific State law.

Schools may disclose, without consent, "directory" information such as a student's name, address, telephone number, date and place of birth, honors and awards, and dates of attendance. However, schools must tell parents and eligible students about directory information and allow parents and eligible students a reasonable amount of time to request that the school not disclose directory information about them. Schools must notify parents and eligible students annually of their rights under FERPA. The actual means of notification (special letter, inclusion in a PTA bulletin, student handbook, or newspaper article) is left to the discretion of each school.

Family Policy Compliance Office
U.S. Department of Education
400 Maryland Avenue, SW
Washington, D.C. 20202-4605

Chapter 8

The School Curriculum

Name_____

CLASS REFLECTIONS - The School Curriculum

....

Date:_____   Topic:_____

Description:

_____

_____

_____

_____

_____

Analysis:

_____

_____

_____

_____

_____

_____

Future Impact:

_____

_____

_____

_____

_____

_____

Date:_____   Topic:_____

Description:

_____

_____

_____

_____

_____

Analysis:

_____

_____

_____

_____

_____

Future Impact:

_____

_____

_____

_____

_____

Name_____

Activity 8.1 - Review for Chapter 8

I. Clearly explain or define the following terms, concepts, or acronyms.

- character education:

- curriculum:

- curriculum guide:

- explicit curriculum:

- implicit curriculum:

- integrated curriculum:

- outcomes-based education:

- service learning:

II. What are the five major forces that influence curriculum?

      1.

      2.

      3.

      4.

      5.

III. Identify four issues a teacher must consider when selecting a textbook.

      1.

      2.

      3.

      4.

IV. List three reasons cited by advocates of a national curriculum.

      1.

      2.

      3.

Activity 8.2 - Textbook Evaluation

A basic component of virtually all courses is a textbook. Once selected, the textbook becomes the primary link between the teacher, the student, and the content area. Because of their central role in the educational process, textbooks must be critically evaluated before a choice is made.

For this activity you will evaluate a textbook for the subject area and/or grade level you plan to teach. Only textbooks specifically designed for grades K-12 may be used. College textbooks are not acceptable for this activity. Select a textbook and complete the following evaluation instrument.

Subject Area: _____   Grade Level: _____

Title of the Textbook: _____

Author(s): _____

_____

Publisher: _____

Copyright Date: _____   Edition: _____   Number of Pages: _____

Binding: _____Hardcover   _____Paperback   _____Spiral Binding

Where did you locate the text you used for this activity?

_____

Using the information identified on the other side of this form, how do you rate this text?

_____Excellent   _____Average   _____Poor

_____Above Average   _____Below Average

Comments:

Based on your present knowledge of what should be taught in the subject area and at the grade level you identified, rate the textbook on the following issues. Use the following system:

5 = Excellent   3 = Average   1 = Poor
4 = Above Average   2 = Below Average   U = Unknown

	5	4	3	2	1	U
Cover design_____						
Scope of content covered_____						
Depth of content covered_____						
Logical organization_____						
Objective presentation of material_____						
Up-to-date coverage of content_____						
Clear writing_____						
Appropriate reading level_____						
Objectives are identified throughout_____						
Vocabulary words are highlighted_____						
Review questions are included_____						
References and resources are identified_____						
Illustrations – black and white_____						
Illustrations – color_____						
Diagrams and charts are used_____						
Illustrations/pictures are multicultural_____						
Illustrations/pictures include the disabled____						
Technology is addressed throughout_____						
Teacher's edition is available_____						
Support materials are available_____						

Resource 8.1

The New Jersey Core Curriculum Content Standards

Introduction

The New Jersey Core Curriculum Content Standards were first adopted by the State Board of Education in 1996. The standards describe what students should know and be able to do upon completion of a thirteen-year public education. Revised every five years, the standards provide local school districts with clear and specific benchmarks for student achievement in nine content areas. Developed by panels of teachers, administrators, parents, students, and representatives from higher education, business, and the community, the standards were influenced by national standards, research-based practice, and student need. The standards define a "Thorough and Efficient Education" as guaranteed in 1875 by the New Jersey Constitution.

The New Jersey Core Curriculum Content Standards (NJCCCS) On-Line

All of the New Jersey Core Curriculum Content Standards, and the supporting Frameworks, can be found at the New Jersey Department of Education web site: (www.nj.gov/njded/aps/cccs). The nine content area pages are:

- Career Education and Consumer, Family and Life Skills
- Comprehensive Health and Physical Education
- Language Arts Literacy
- Mathematics
- Science
- Social Studies
- Technology
- Visual and Performing Arts
- World Languages

Each of the content area pages contains the following information:
- New Jersey Core Curriculum Content Standards
- Curriculum Framework
- Professional Development Opportunities
- Assessment
- Applicable Statutes and Regulations
- National and International Standards
- Frequently Asked Questions
- Professional Associations and Activities
- Resources

Resource 8.2

New Jersey Core Curriculum Content Standards Outline:
Example – Language Arts Literacy

• **Language Arts Literacy** •

Standards and Strands

There are five language arts literacy standards, each of which has lettered strands and learning expectations for each grade level in grades K-8, as well as a combined cluster for grades 9-12. The standards and strands are outlined below:

3.1 Reading
- A. Concepts About Print
- B. Phonological Awareness
- C. Decoding and Word Recognition
- D. Fluency
- E. Reading Strategies (before, during, and after reading)
- F. Vocabulary and Concept Development
- G. Comprehension Skills and Response to Text
- H. Inquiry and Research

3.2 Writing
- A. Writing as a Process
- B. Writing as a Product
- C. Mechanics, Spelling, and Handwriting
- D. Writing Forms, Audiences, and Purposes

3.3 Speaking
- A. Discussion
- B. Questioning (Inquiry) and Contributing
- C. Word Choice
- D. Oral Presentation

3.4 Listening
- A. Active Listening
- B. Listening Comprehension

3.5 Viewing and Media Literacy
- A. Constructing Meaning
- B. Visual and Verbal Messages
- C. Living with Media

Resource 8.3

FAQ – Language Arts Literacy

The following material is from the "Frequently Asked Questions" section of the NJ Core Curriculum Content Standards for Language Arts Literacy.

Q. The State Board adopted the revised Language Arts Literacy Core Curriculum Content Standards (CCCS) in April 2004. When will they be reviewed for update?

A. The CCCS are to be reviewed every five years from their implementation. The revised language arts literacy, mathematics, science, visual and performing arts, comprehensive health and physical education, world languages, technological literacy, and career education and consumer, family and life skills standards will be reviewed for update in 2009.

Q. How will teachers have an opportunity to become informed about the standards and frameworks?

A. Several copies of the standards and frameworks documents were provided to the building administrator in each public school. In addition, chief school administrators, education associations, and institutions of higher education have received copies. All standards and frameworks documents are on the department's Web site.

Q. The Standards and Assessment proposal expands the statewide testing. How do you justify taking up so much of the students' time with testing?

A. It is generally recognized that whatever is emphasized in testing is the material that will be emphasized in instruction. It is critical for New Jersey's future that the level of learning in the state's public schools be academically rigorous and internationally competitive for all students. New Jersey's Core Curriculum Content Standards set the content-specific goals for that learning, but it is the statewide assessment system that both encourages teachers and students to aim for those standards and also measures our progress in achieving them. New Jersey's statewide assessment system is consistent with federal guidelines which support high state standards.

Q. What is the purpose of the curriculum frameworks?

A. The curriculum frameworks serve as a bridge between the general goals stated in the Core Curriculum Content Standards and the greater specificity required by district curricula. More specifically, the frameworks do the following:
- Illustrate how to teach the content standards and indicators at various levels through high- quality instructional activities that can also assist districts to align curriculum;
- Provide a guide to implementing the standards for teachers and administrators;
- Help translate a vision of exemplary education into practice; and
- Provide guidance on the major issues of standards-based reform, on the process of systemic change, and on the areas of content, instruction, and assessment.

Q. Are the framework documents useful for teachers of students with special needs?

A. Yes, the frameworks will have separate chapters discussing specific ways the content can be modified and/or adapted for students with disabilities, students of limited English proficiency, and gifted and talented students.

Q. What is the Report of the NJ Task Force on Middle Grade Literacy Education?

A. The Task Force was created to:
- Initiate a statewide conversation about literacy education in grades 4-8
- Produce a consensus document that provides background information to guide policy and practice along with specific recommendations for action.
- Improve the quality of literacy instruction in grades 4-8.

The recommendations, presented in May 2004, center on Implementing Effective Practices, Professional development, Pre-service Teacher Education and Certification, and Assessment. For more information, go to:
http://www.state.nj.us/njded/genfo/midlteracy.htm

Q. Why were the Language Arts Literacy Core Curriculum Standards changed in 2004?

A. The driving force was the required testing in Language Arts each year in grades 3 through 8 by 2005-2006. As a result, the changes focused on developing individual grade-level Cumulative Progress Indicators (CPIs) for the 5 Language Arts Literacy Core Curriculum Content Standards at grades 5, 6, 7, and 8. Previously, those grade-levels were clustered at grades (5 and 6) and at grades (7 and 8).

Chapter 9

Instruction in American Classrooms

....

Date:_____   Topic:_____

Description:

_____

_____

_____

_____

_____

Analysis:

_____

_____

_____

_____

_____

Future Impact:

_____

_____

_____

_____

_____

Date:_____ Topic:_____

Description:

_____

_____

_____

_____

_____

Analysis:

_____

_____

_____

_____

_____

Future Impact:

_____

_____

_____

_____

_____

Activity 9.1 - Review for Chapter 9

I. Clearly explain or define the following terms, concepts, or acronyms.

- assessment:

- authentic assessment:

- classroom management:

- cooperative learning:

- discovery learning:

- equitable distribution:

- instructional alignment:

- instructional goals:

- modeling:

- personal teacher efficacy:

- portfolio:

- wait-time:

II. What are the five areas in which effective teachers differ from less effective teachers?

1.

2.

3.

4.

5.

Name_____

Activity 9.2 - The Effective Teacher

I. Describe 3 <u>personal characteristics</u> effective teachers possess.

     1._____

     _____

     2._____

     _____

     3._____

     _____

II. Describe 3 ways effective teachers <u>organize their classrooms</u> so <u>students can learn</u>.

     1._____

     _____

     2._____

     _____

     3._____

     _____

III. Describe 3 <u>instructional strategies</u> that effective teachers use.

1._____

_____

2._____

_____

3._____

_____

IV. Describe 3 ways effective teachers <u>assess their students</u>.

1._____

_____

2._____

_____

3._____

_____

Name_____

Activity 9.3 - Beginning to Think About Lesson Planning

Think about how you would teach a 15 to 30 minute lesson that is highly interesting to a class of 20 students. Select any lesson and identify the following items:

Subject Area_____ Grade Level_____

Lesson Topic or Title_____

_____

Major Lesson Objective:

_____

_____

Sub-Objectives:

_____

_____

_____

_____

Number and List the Steps in Teaching the Lesson:

_____

_____

_____

_____

Resource 9.1

A Catalog of Teaching Methods

- **Constructivist teaching** - teaching is based on the students prior knowledge and the processes they use to construct knowledge.

- **Cross-age tutoring** - an arrangement where older students tutor younger students.

- **Direct instruction** - an instructional method that focuses on the transmission of knowledge and skills from the teacher to the student.

- **Discovery learning** - allows the student to explore a topic so he/she can discover knowledge.

- **Inquiry learning** - the student is allowed to explore and inquire about subjects to develop their own answers to problems.

- **Mastery teaching** - the belief that all students can learn the material if given sufficient time and if the material is presented in small incremental steps.

- **Modeling** - the process of "thinking out loud" to show the students the reasoning involved in learning new material.
- **Peer-mediated instruction** - approaches such as cooperative learning and group work that use social interaction to facilitate learning.

- **Peer-tutoring** - the students tutor other students in their classroom or at the same grade level.

- **Scaffolding** - the teacher builds on the student's current level of understanding and ability to help move them forward.

- **Team teaching** - an arrangement where two or three teachers teach a group of students, usually equal to the number they would have in their own classrooms.

Resource 9.2

Learning through Discussion:
Designing Tasks for Critical Inquiry and Reflective Learning
Ngeow, Karen - Kong, Yoon-San
(ERIC Digest – ED477611)

Discussion is very often used as a tool in classrooms. When designed properly and used thoughtfully, discussion tasks can be an effective learning tool that promote creativity, as well as generate meaningful interaction and understanding for the learner. Well-designed discussion tasks lead to progressive knowledge-seeking inquiry (Scardamalia & Bereiter, 1994) or expansive learning (Engestrom, 1999) where learners are actively synthesizing new information with prior knowledge and experiences in the process of creating not only new knowledge but also new understanding of the learning process.

Teachers use discussion tasks to achieve different goals: critical inquiry, debate and reflection. However, it is not difficult to ensure that "learning" will naturally occur in a discussion task. Perkins 1986) reminds teachers that the meaningfulness of a task is not found in the problem or task itself; rather, the learner has to impose his or her own meanings and defines individual goals during the process of accomplishing the task. In other words, the purpose of learning within this context is not to "get it right," but to produce something meaningful through critical inquiry, debate and reflection.

TYPES OF DISCUSSION TASKS

The move to understanding discussion as more than an instructional tool that encourages learners to talk has implications for the design of discussion tasks. Hacker and Niederhauser (2000) argue that effective learning comes about through teachers' thoughtful design and use of instructional strategies.

Below are four major discussion tasks designed for classroom use, with a description of teachers' roles and learning strategies to be adopted by the discussants.

GUIDED DISCUSSION TASK

The goal of guided or directed discussion tasks is to give learners a chance to develop critical thinking, clear oral expression, as well as experience in posing and responding to questions.

Stage 1: The teacher poses a discussion question to the whole class. Guidelines are given on discussion etiquette and criteria for evaluation. Each learner contributes an original answer in response to the discussion question.

Stage 2: Learners offer responses or questions to each other's contributions as a means of broadening the discussion's scope.

Stage 3: Learners present their views or the views of their groups, either orally or in writing at the end of the guided discussion task.

INQUIRY-BASED DISCUSSION TASK

This task guides learners through a series of questions to discover some relationship or principle, and to help learners acquire reasoning skills to analyze new information. The beginning stages are similar to those in the guided discussion task, but in an inquiry-based discussion task, learners are further required to bring in information and issues from outside the textbook or classroom for discussion.

Stage 4: The teacher poses a discussion issue that requires argumentative reasoning and elaboration. Learners are required to go beyond the textbook to evaluate this discussion issue.

Stage 5: Learners identify and highlight main issues relevant to the discussion. In doing so, they appraise the new information they have acquired for its validity and relevance as well as test their ideas against insights and perspectives provided by their peers.

Stage 6: Learners summarize the discussion in light of other discussants' reactions and interpretations. This helps them to synthesize supporting and opposing ideas that are relevant to the issue.

REFLECTIVE DISCUSSION TASK

Teachers use this task to help learners become more cognizant of the learning process and to enable them to derive meaningful insights from their learning experiences.

Stage 7: The teacher asks learners to prepare a self-analysis of their roles and contributions to the discussion process.

Stage 8: Learners analyze "how they learn" and think about what will help them be more effective in future discussions. They respond to introspective questions that help them to reflect on conditions that facilitated or hindered their learning processes.

EXPLORATORY DISCUSSION TASK

This task assists learners by honing their analytical skills to arrive at alternative explanations in a variety of real-world scenarios. Here, learners are compelled to first examine their personal opinions, suppositions or assumptions and then visualize alternatives to these assumptions.

Stage 9: The teacher poses a real-world problem that requires learners to consider - in context – the premises or ideas they have been discussing.

Stage 10: Learners assess their beliefs or opinions and evaluate how alternatives to these beliefs and opinions apply in a variety of real-world situations.

CONCLUSION

The learning-through-discussion framework shares aspects of Bereiter's (1994) concept of progressive discourse, where the goals are for learners to first develop their individual thinking, then suspend these opinions to consider alternatives, and later negotiate meaning with other discussants to arrive at a shared understanding of the issues at hand. With thoughtful and well-designed discussion tasks, teachers can help students attain learning goals of critical inquiry, debate and reflection.

ONLINE RESOURCES FOR TEACHERS

Using Questioning and Discussion in the Classroom: Resources compiled by the UMDNJ Academic Information Technology Advisory Committee. This site contains key aspects of successful discussions and an FAQ list for teachers interested in using discussions.
www.umdnj.edu/meg/traditional_discussion_questioning.htm

Fostering Effective Classroom Discussions: A selective list of online resources - by Barton, Heilker and Rutkowski. Of particular interest here are sites on the use of questioning techniques that facilitate good discussion practices.
www.mhhe.com/socscience/english/tc/pt/discussion/resources.htm

Class Discussions - by The Center for the Advancement of Teaching, Illinois State University. This site has resources on using icebreakers and group activities to facilitate collaboration amongst students in discussion activities.
www.cat.ilstu.edu/teaching_tips/classd.shtml

Assessing Discussion: Active and Collaborative Learning. This is a resource site for Valencia faculty. It has an instrument and some assessment guidelines for evaluating student contributions in class discussions.
http://faculty.valencia.cc.fl.us/pbishop/lcrb/lcrsrc_clsinter.htm Classroom

(References: See ED 477611)

Chapter 10

Joining the Profession

Name_____

CLASS REFLECTIONS - Joining the Profession

....

Date:_____   Topic:_____

Description:

_____

_____

_____

_____

_____

Analysis:

_____

_____

_____

_____

_____

_____

Future Impact:

_____

_____

_____

_____

_____

_____

Date:_____   Topic:_____

Description:

_____

_____

_____

_____

_____

Analysis:

_____

_____

_____

_____

_____

Future Impact:

_____

_____

_____

_____

_____

Name_____

Activity 10.1 - Review for Chapter 10

I. Clearly explain or define the following terms, concepts, or acronyms.

• alternative licensure:

• certification:

• general pedagogical knowledge:

• INTASC:

• licensure:

• NBPTS:

• pedagogical content knowledge:

• Praxis I:

• Praxis II:

• professional portfolio:

• resume´:

II. What are the four kinds of knowledge expert teachers possess?

    1.

    2.

    3.

    4.

III. Classroom management is one of the greatest concerns of the beginning teacher. Explain why.

144

Name_____

Activity 10.2 - Content Area Professional Organizations

Below is a list of the major professional organizations in the content areas. Select one of these organizations and go to their web site. Review the material at the site. Based on the material provided, you are to prepare a <u>one-page</u> information sheet about the organization and their web site.

The paper must be <u>word processed</u> in <u>12 point type</u> and be <u>double spaced</u>. The title of the paper is the name of the organization you select.

- American Alliance for Health, Physical Education, Recreation and Dance
    www.aahperd.org
- American Council on the Teaching of Foreign Languages
    www.actfl.org
- International Reading Association
    www.reading.org
- International Society for Technology in Education
    www.iste.org
- National Art Education Association
    www.naea-reston.org
- National Association for Music Education
    www.menc.org
- National Association for the Education of Young Children
    www.naeyc.org
- National Council for the Social Studies
    www.ncss.org
- National Council of Teachers of English
    www.ncte.org
- National Council of Teachers of Mathematics
    www.nctm.org
- National Science Teachers Association
    www.nsta.org

Resource 10.1

Selected Highlights from *The Condition of Education 2004* (National Center for Educational Statistics)

The Condition of Education 2004, the latest edition of NCES's annual congressionally mandated progress reports, conveys current information on 38 indicators that cover all aspects of U.S. education, including trends in enrollments, student achievement, dropout rates, degree attainment, long-term outcomes of education, and education financing. Here are some highlights from this year's edition.

Paying for College

This year's special analysis examines recent changes in the ways that families pay for the college education of full-time, dependent undergraduates. According to *Paying for College, Changes Between 1990 and 2000 for Full-Time Dependent Undergraduate,* college prices and financial aid both increased during the 1990s. During the 1990s, increases in tuition and fees outpaced both inflation and growth in the median family income. The same period saw an increase in the percentage of full-time, dependent undergraduates who received financial aid (consisting primarily of grants, student loans, or both).

The analysis shows that between 1990 and 2000, the percentage of full-time dependent undergraduates receiving aid in the form of grants increased from 45 to 57 percent. Because grant aid is not repaid, it reduces the price to attend college. However, the growth in grant aid was not enough to fully offset price increases. Use of student loans also increased during this period, with the percentage of borrowers among full-time, dependent undergraduates rising from 30 to 45 percent. The growth in grant and loan aid was enough to offset or exceed price increases except for students in the highest income groups attending 2- and 4-year public institutions. Financial aid increases occurred partly because the 1992 Reauthorization of the Higher Education Act broadened eligibility for need-based aid, raised loan limits, and made unsubsidized loans available to students regardless of need. In addition, states and institutions increased their grant aid.

Elementary/Secondary Education Enrollments

The Condition of Education provides a picture of both progress and ongoing challenges in U.S. education. On the topic of participation in elementary and secondary education, enrollments are on the increase as a result of rising immigration and the baby boom echo. Many public schools are offering prekindergarten programs as well; in 2000–01, 35 percent of public elementary schools offered such programs, and over 800,000 children participated. Thirteen percent of public elementary schools had full-day programs, 19 percent had halfday programs, and 3 percent had both. Between 1977 and 2001, kindergarten enrollments increased, with the majority of enrolled children shifting from half day to full-day programs. A continuing challenge was reflected in the distribution of minority students in 2003, with about half of Black and Hispanic 4th-graders (compared with 5 percent of White 4th-graders) enrolled in schools where 75 percent or more of the students came from families living in poverty. Similarly, about 40 percent of Black and Hispanic students attended schools in which 90 percent or more of the students were minorities.

Student Achievement

The success of our education system ultimately depends upon the academic achievement of *all* students. While students with multiple risk factors make considerable progress in reading and mathematics from the beginning of kindergarten through the 3rd grade, they start behind students with no risk factors and make less progress. Improvements have occurred in the performance of elementary and secondary students over the past decade, though not in all grades and all subjects. The reading performance of 8th-graders increased between 1992 and 2003, while no change occurred for 4th-graders. The writing performance of both 4th- and 8th-graders improved between 1998 and 2002, although no significant change was detected among 12th graders' writing. Between 1990 and 2003, the mathematics performance of 4th and 8th graders improved each time an assessment was administered (about every 4 years).

The success of our education system is also reflected in students' rates of progress toward the completion of high school and their engagement in further learning or the workforce. In 2003, 13 percent of all persons ages 16–24 were neither enrolled in school nor working. This was a decrease from 16 percent in 1986. During the same period, the percentage of poor youth who were neither enrolled in school nor working decreased more than the percentage of nonpoor youth. The annual rate of dropping out of high school declined during the 1970s and 1980s but remained unchanged for all income groups during the 1990s. Among students entering postsecondary education as freshmen in fall 2000, 28 percent were required to take some remedial coursework. Students who take any remedial coursework are less likely to earn a bachelor's degree or certificate than those who take none. Overall, bachelor's degree completion rates have remained steady over time; 53 percent earn a bachelor's degree within 5 years. However, the likelihood of still being enrolled for a bachelor's degree at the end of 5 years has increased. Women have earned more than half of all bachelor's degrees every year since 1981–82. They still trail men in certain fields but have made substantial gains since 1970–71 and have taken the lead in some fields that were previously male-dominated.

Salient Features of Schooling

The Condition of Education also looks at salient features of the schooling process—including courses taken, teacher qualifications, choice of schools available to parents and families. The percentage of high school graduates who

148

had completed advanced courses in science and mathematics increased between 1982 and 2000. In science, the increase was from 35 percent to 63 percent of graduates; in mathematics, the increase was from 26 percent to 45 percent of graduates. In 1999–2000, high school students in high-poverty and high-minority public schools were more often taught English, science, and mathematics by out-of-field teachers than their peers in low-poverty and low minority schools. In middle schools, the difference was evident only in social studies where the students in low-minority schools were more likely to be taught by an out-of-field teacher than those in high-minority schools.

Between 1993 and 2003, the percentage of students in grades 1–12 whose parents enrolled them in chosen (as opposed to assigned) public schools increased from 11 to 15 percent, while the percentage attending assigned public schools decreased from 80 to 74 percent. The percentage of students attending private schools also increased; this increase was, however, smaller than the increase in the percentage of students attending chosen public schools. The parents of 51 percent of students reported that they had the option of sending their child to a chosen public school. The parents of 24 percent of students said that they moved to a new neighborhood so that their children could attend a particular school.

Between 1991–92 and 2000–01, total expenditures per student enrolled in public elementary/secondary education increased by 25 percent in constant 2000–01 dollars, from $6,950 in 1991–92 to $8,700 in 2000–01. During the same period, current expenditures, which consist of total expenditures less capital expenditures, increased by 24 percent.

Postsecondary Education

In the next 10 years, continued increases in undergraduate enrollments are projected, with enrollments rising faster in 4-year institutions compared with 2-year institutions, among full-time students compared with part-time students, and among women compared with men. The college courses in which students earn the most credits have remained relatively stable over the past three decades. For 1972, 1982, and 1992 high school graduates who went on to earn a bachelor's degree, 21 of the top 30 college courses were the same (these courses were in the areas of the humanities and languages, science and mathematics, social science, business, music performance, physical education, and student teaching). The number of course enrollments in distance education increased from 1.7 to 3.1 million between 1997–98 and 2000–01. About half of all distance education course enrollments in 2000–01 were in 2-year public colleges.

Resource 10.2

Representative Teacher Interview Questions

Administrators were asked to share interview questions they frequently ask when interviewing prospective teachers. Their responses are grouped in broad categories.

I. Professional Experiences

- Discuss your student teaching experience. What did you like/dislike?
- Tell me about your most challenging experience while working with children or in the classroom?
- Discuss your feelings/experience in reference to working in an urban setting.
- Tell us about your other school-related experiences such as extra-curricular activities, committees, curriculum development, etc.
- What experience have you had with students from culturally diverse backgrounds?

II. Instructional Skills

- Describe the best lesson you have taught. Why was it successful?
- Describe the teaching techniques or strategies that are most effective for you.
- Describe your typical lesson. What does it include and who participates - how do they participate?
- How would you include cooperative teaming in class teaching?
- How will you instruct/challenge students with varying abilities?
- What techniques would you use to be sure that pupils understand?
- How can individualization actually be practiced in the classroom?
- How do you know whether pupils understand what you are teaching during a lesson?
- What techniques do you use to keep pupils actively involved during a lesson?
- How would you assess your effectiveness as a teacher?
- How do you deal with the unmotivated student?
- Tell me about some specific motivational strategies you use to get students excited about teaming.
- What would I see in your class?
- What is the most important "thing" a student could learn in your class?
- Explain how you have changed your lesson plan preparation and presentation as you have gained experience.
- How do you meet the needs of individual students in your classroom?.
- How do you differentiate instruction?

III. Technology / Computer Skills

- How would you apply technology to enhance daily instruction and increase student learning / achievement?
- How would you (or have you) incorporate(d) technology in you classroom?
- Explain your skills using a computer - address classroom management (ex: grade book), instructional, other.
- Are you comfortable with the use of technology in the classroom?
- What are your computer skills? What computer software have you used?

IV. Classroom Discipline

- Describe your philosophy regarding discipline.
- What was the most challenging discipline problem you've encountered and how did you handle it?
- What techniques would you use to handle discipline problems that may arise in your classroom?
- How would you deal with a student who disrupts?
- What kinds of rules do you have in your classroom? How are they established?
- What do you feel are the most important factors in classroom control?

V. Classroom Management

- What is your classroom management plan/style? What are your goals?
- I walk into your classroom; what would it look, feel, and sound like?
- Describe what you would consider to be a model classroom.
- How would you describe your learning environment?
- Describe your organization and management strategies.
- Share three interesting techniques used in the classroom.
- What role does classroom management play in the educational process?

VI. Knowledge of Content/Materials

- What coursework have you taken that has made you especially suited for this position ?
- Are there any materials you have used that you find are especially effective for slow learners or bright students?
- What kinds of tests do you like to give?
- Describe your educational background and teaching experience related to your subject area.
- How do you stay current in your field?

VII. Planning Skills

- How well organized are you? Why is organization important for a teacher?
- What do you include in your daily lesson plans?
- How closely do you follow your plans?

- Describe for me the organization that goes into your planning for a lesson. I'm sitting in the back of your classroom; in some detail tell me what I see as you implement the lesson just described.
- What are some of the considerations you make when planning your lessons?
- How do you go about planning a unit?

VIII. Relationships with Administrators, Staff, Parents, and Students

- Are you willing to sponsor any extra-curricular activities?
- Would you describe an outstanding teacher to me?
- What kind of person do you like to work for?
- Describe how you could be an effective communicator as part of the school community. (parents , staff)
- Describe your approach with a parent who is upset with you - and you know you are right.
- What are some methods of communicating student progress to parents other than report cards?
- How do you feel about parent contact?
- How would your students describe you as a teacher?
- How do you want students to view you?
- Do you want pupils to like you? Why?
- How can you get students to be excited about learning?
- Should a teacher intentionally use humor in the classroom? How do you use humor in the classroom?
- If I were a child, why would I want to be in your classroom?
- Do you have a specific grade level/age that you prefer to teach? Why?

IX. Personal Qualities

- Why have you selected teaching as a profession?
- Tell us about yourself and why are you interested in this school district and/or position.
- What are your career goals--short term and long term?
- What do you consider to be your major strength you bring to the classroom?
- What do you believe is the one area you want to work on improving?
- What distinguishes you from other candidates?
- What do you bring to the community besides your educational background?
- Is there anything you would like to add to help us evaluate your candidacy?
- Describe yourself as "the teacher".
- What makes you an effective teacher?
- What do you enjoy most about teaching?
- If I were to contact your references, what do you think they would say about you?
- Tell me three things you believe about teaching.
- Describe yourself with three adjectives and explain why they were chosen.
- What is your most successful accomplishment?
- Describe your fears of being a teacher.
- Would you describe yourself as a team player or individual achiever?

Chapter 11

Traditional Educational Technology

Name_____

CLASS REFLECTIONS - Traditional Technology

....

Date:_____   Topic:_____

Description:

_____

_____

_____

_____

_____

Analysis:

_____

_____

_____

_____

_____

Future Impact:

_____

_____

_____

_____

_____

Date:_____ **Topic:**_____

Description:

_____

_____

_____

_____

_____

Analysis:

_____

_____

_____

_____

_____

Future Impact:

_____

_____

_____

_____

_____

Name_____

Activity 11.1 - Review for Chapter 11

I. Clearly explain or define the following terms, concepts, or acronyms.

• camcorder:

• cognitive map:

• interactive bulletin board:

• learning center:

• multipurpose board:

• video projector:

• visual presenter:

II. What are the five areas of instructional technology identified in the text?

    1.

    2.

    3.

    4.

    5.

III. Identify three advantages of using a textbook in your teaching.

    1.

    2.

    3.

IV. Identify three advantages of using an overhead projector in your teaching.

    1.

    2.

    3.

V. Identify the four major types of classroom bulletin boards.

    1.

    2.

    3.

    4.

Activity 11.2 - Using Traditional Technology

Imagine that you are teaching in the subject area and at the grade level that you prefer. Complete the following form describing how you could use the identified traditional technology tools in your classroom.

I. Textbooks (Print Technology)

Subject Area_____ Grade Level_____

Lesson Topic: _____

How will you use the technology?

What is the advantage for the student if you use this technology?

What is the advantage for you as the teacher?

II. Overhead Projector (Audiovisual Technology)

Subject Area_____ Grade Level_____

Lesson Topic: _____

How will you use the technology?

What is the advantage for the student if you use this technology?

What is the advantage for you as the teacher?

III. Bulletin Board (Display Technology)

Subject Area_____ Grade Level_____

Lesson Topic: _____

How will you use the technology?

What is the advantage for the student if you use this technology?

What is the advantage for you as the teacher?

Resource 11.1

Copyright Questions and Answers

Federal legislation has clearly, and with specificity, addressed the area of copyright for print materials produced in the form of books and periodicals as it relates to educational institutions. However, questions and concerns abound regarding copyright in many of the other areas of Instructional Technology. Here we address some of the questions most frequently asked by teachers regarding the use of copyrighted materials in an educational institution.

Note: The material included in this section is provided only for informational purposes and is not to be interpreted as legal advice. In all cases, the district or school's legal counsel should be consulted when legal answers are warranted.

Q. 1 - What are the general guidelines for showing media materials in a classroom setting ?

Videos, films, filmstrips, etc., regardless of whether they have been purchased, leased, or rented, may be used for face-to-face instruction in classrooms as a part of the identified course curriculum. They may not, however, be shown for recreational or entertainment purposes or as a "reward" to students without a "nontheatrical-public-performance license."

Q. 2 - Am I allowed to use a video in a classroom that includes a "For Home Use Only" warning label or screen?

Yes, providing it meets the criteria identified above. The "For Home Use Only" label disallows showing the video for a "nontheatrical-public performance" without a license.

Q. 3 - May I record a television program and show it in class as a part of my course?

Yes, providing it is a program that was a broadcast transmission to the "general public." [This excludes premium-pay broadcasts such as Disney, Showtime, HBO, etc.] In addition, you must meet the following requirements: The program may be shown once and repeated once for reinforcement within ten teaching days of the broadcast. The copy may only be retained for forty-five calendar days from the date of broadcast. [Some "educational broadcasts" extend this time.]

Q. 4 - Am I allowed to copy a commercial computer software program that I buy ?

No. All commercial computer software is purchased with some type of licensing agreement. A "signed agreement" requires the purchaser to return a warranty agreement card to the publisher. An "implied agreement" is a piece of paper in the package that states "by using this software you agree to the conditions of purchase." A "shrink-wrap" agreement states that the purchaser is bound by the conditions of the license (usually visible through the shrink-wrap) if the package is opened. A "click wrap" agreement is shown on the screen when the software is installed. The user must click the "accept" button agreeing to the licensing conditions before the software can be installed. In all cases, one of the conditions is that you agree not to copy the software.

Two exceptions should be noted. (1) The purchaser is allowed to make a backup copy of the software for "archival" purposes. This copy may only be used if the original is destroyed. (2) If a site license is purchased, the license will stipulate the number of additional copies that may be made.

Q. 5 - Is there any type of computer software that I am allowed to copy?

Yes, there are three types. (1) "Shareware" is software that has been copyrighted, but has been released to the public on a try-it-before-you-buy-it basis. The author expects to be paid for the software. Payment varies and is on the honor system. (2) "Freeware" does not require payment by the user, but the author wants the copyright notice displayed and does not want the program modified. (3) "Public domain" software has been released to the public by its author and may be copied and used by anyone, without restrictions.

Q. 6 - I want to duplicate, for each student in the class, an outline of the state map and a list of the twelve largest cities in the state for an assignment. Is this allowed?

Yes, "simple facts" cannot be copyrighted. This category includes outline maps and lists of names such as streets, cities, states, etc. Other items that are included in this category are distance charts, mathematical tables, a list of presidents, outline diagrams, and any item that is a basic list of facts.

Q. 7 - A magazine ran a series of articles, in six issues, following the drug rehabilitation of a student. I want to duplicate these articles as a booklet for use with my eighth grade health class. Is this educational use allowed?

No. This undertaking would violate two restrictions of the fair use multiple copy guidelines: (1) You are not allowed to create anthologies and (2) you are not allowed to take more that three articles from the issues of an annual volume.

162

Q. 8 - I just purchased a copy of a video that is going to be used by other teachers as well as myself. May I make a back-up copy in case something happens to the original? It was expensive and I will not circulate the back-up copy.

No. Archival or "back-up" copies may only be made of computer software. When a video is purchased you have the right to use that specific tape for the "life of tape." When the tape no longer works, you must purchase another copy.

Q. 9 - What are "public domain" materials?

Public domain is the exact opposite of copyright. Copyright has many restrictions. Public domain has no restrictions. In the United States, eventually, all intellectual property enters the public domain. These materials may be used by anyone.

With some exceptions (depending on the year that the work was copyrighted), anything published more that 75 years before January of the current year or any work entirely created and published by a U.S. Government Agency is in the public domain. Consequently, most government documents and most of the materials on the U.S. Federal Government web sites are in the public domain. Some entire sites are in the public domain (e.g.: The White House, the Consumer Information Catalog, etc.).

Q. 10 - The students in my class are each preparing a multimedia presentation on a country. Are they allowed to use parts of commercial multimedia products as part of their project?

Yes. CONFU (The Conference on Fair Use) has developed Fair Use Guidelines for Educational Multimedia. These guidelines have the endorsement of the U.S. Copyright Office. They state that "students may incorporate portions of lawfully acquired copyrighted works when producing their own multimedia projects for a course."

Resource 11.2

Visual Presenters

Overview

Visual presenters are also called document cameras, presentation cameras, and visualizers. They are used in traditional instructional settings as well as in conjunction with video conferencing systems. Their wide appeal is due to the variety of materials that can be shown with this technology. These include all paper documents (books, periodicals, written assignments, newspaper clippings, etc.), transparencies, photographs, 35mm slides and realia (3-dimensional objects ranging from small tools and coins to plants or a live worm).

A typical visual presenter consists of (1) a stage on which the object is placed, (2) a video camera mounted above the stage, (3) directional lights that illuminate the stage from above, and (4) a light built into the stage that allows it to function as an overhead projector for transparencies and slides.

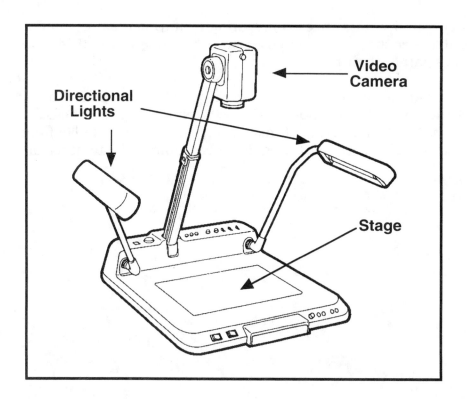

How To Use Visual Presenters

The visual presenter is an input technology, and therefore must be coupled with an output technology such as a television monitor or a video projector. Due to the variety of models, the operator's manual for the specific model being used should be consulted. The following are general directions for the two basic uses: presenting opaque materials and presenting transparent materials.

To Present Opaque Materials

Opaque materials are items that light will not project through. This includes books, periodicals, drawings, and all three-dimensional objects such as tools, coins, small plants, insects, etc.

1. Unlock the column arm and set the camera head in position (if required for the model being used).
2. Plug-in the power cord.
3. Connect the visual presenter to the selected output device--TV monitor or video projector. [See the operator's manual.]
4. Turn on the output device.
5. Turn on the visual presenter.
6. Turn on the "directional lights."
7. Place the object to be presented on the "stage."
8. Adjust the "focus" and "zoom" to achieve the optimum image.
9. USE the visual presenter to present opaque objects.
10. Reverse the steps for "shut-down."

To Present Transparent Materials

The most common type of transparent materials are overhead transparencies. These can be either commercial or teacher-made.

1. Unlock the column arm and set the camera head in position (if required for the model being used).
2. Plug-in the power cord.
3. Connect the visual presenter to the selected output device--TV monitor or video projector. [See the operator's manual for the model being used.]
4. Turn on the output device.
5. Turn on the visual presenter.
6. Turn on the "stage light."
7. Place the object to be presented on the "stage."
8. Adjust the "focus" and "zoom" to achieve the optimum image.
9. USE the visual presenter to present opaque objects.
10. Reverse the steps for "shut-down."

Chapter 12

Contemporary Educational Technology

Name_____

CLASS REFLECTIONS - Contemporary Technology

....

Date:_____   Topic:_____

Description:

_____

_____

_____

_____

_____

Analysis:

_____

_____

_____

_____

_____

Future Impact:

_____

_____

_____

_____

_____

_____

_____

Date:_____   Topic:_____

Description:

_____

_____

_____

_____

_____

Analysis:

_____

_____

_____

_____

_____

Future Impact:

_____

_____

_____

_____

_____

Activity 12.1 - Review for Chapter 12

I. Clearly explain or define the following terms, concepts, or acronyms.

- AUP:

- educational portal:

- electronic portfolio:

- electronic whiteboard:

- Inspiration:

- ISTE:

- Kid Pix:

- NETS:

- WebQuests:

- wireless technology:

Activity 12.2 - Exploring Web Sites

For this activity you are to visit three web sites that are especially valuable to you as a future teacher. After you enter the web site you are to explore several of the links. Then choose two of the links and write a brief explanation of what you found at those links. Identify how you could use this site in the future.

Site One – Refdesk   **www.refdesk.com**

Name of first link:

What did you find at that link?

Name of second link:

What did you find at that link?

How can you use this site in the future?

Site Two – Dr. LeBeau's Web Site   **www.suelebeau.com**

Name of first link:

What did you find at that link?

Name of second link:

What did you find at that link?

How can you use this site in the future?

Site Three – Education World   **www.educationworld.com**

Name of first link:

What did you find at that link?

Name of second link:

What did you find at that link?

How can you use this site in the future?

Resource 12.1

Dr. LeBeau's Web Site
www.suelebeau.com

Dr. LeBeau's Web Site is an excellent on-line resource for teachers. The pages in this section, which follow one (1) sequence at Dr. LeBeau's site, are intended to demonstrate the immensity and scope of this highly recommended site by a New Jersey educator.

Dr. LeBeau's HomePage

A Resource for Teachers, Students and Curious Adults

EDUCATION RESOURCES	SEARCH ENGINES	COOL LINKS FOR KIDS
TECHNOLOGY LINKS	READING RESOURCES	ALL ABOUT WRITING
SCIENCE LINKS	MATH LINKS FOR EVERYONE	SOCIAL STUDIES LINKS
GEOGRAPHY & PLACES IN THE WORLD	CELEBRATIONS BY THE MONTH	SCHOOL LEADERS & SUPERVISORS
JUST FOR PARENTS	SEARCH THIS WEBSITE	MY WORKSHOP OFFERINGS

Selections for
EDUCATION RESOURCES

GENERAL TEACHER RESOURCES	SEARCHABLE TEACHER LESSON PLANS	JUST FOR THE PRIMARY GRADES
GRAPHIC ORGANIZERS	ASSESSMENT AND RUBRICS WEBSITES	CHARACTER ED & ANTI-BULLYING
JUST FOR THE NEW TEACHER	CLASSROOM MANAGEMENT & DISCIPLINE	FIRST DAY OF SCHOOL IDEAS
ON-LINE TOOLS FOR TEACHERS	SEPTEMBER 11th	TEACHING WITH THE ARTS
ESL & FOREIGN LANGUAGE LINKS	PROFESSIONAL ORGANIZATIONS	E-NEWSLETTERS & PUBLICATIONS
RELIGION CLASS RESOURCES	DISTANCE EDUCATION & HIGHER ED	NO CHILD LEFT BEHIND

Selections for
GENERAL TEACHER RESOURCES

- **Teaching/Classroom Resources**
- Miscellaneous Ed Resources
- Special Ed. & Gifted Resources
- Bloom, MI & Learning Styles
- 100th Day Resources
- Web Cams
- NJ Teachers
- One Room Schoolhouse
- School and Teacher Websites from Around the World

```
┌─────────────────────────────────────────────────────────────┐
│                      Selections for                          │
│               Teaching/Classroom Resources                   │
│                                                              │
│  • Educators' Resources • Teacher Links • Kathy Schrock's Guide for Educators •
│  Teacher TidBytes • The Virtual SchoolHouse • Teachers Net Teachers Helping Teachers
│  • TidBit Things for Teachers • Vicki Blackwell's Teacher Site • Teacher/Pathfinder •
│  Dragonfly HotLinks • Teacher Resources • Educational HotLists from the Franklin
│  Institute • Syvum Online Education and Interactive Learning • Teachers At Work • Gr 3-
│  5 Themes on the Web • Cool Sites for Teachers • Teachers' Lounge • Mini Themes •
│  Teachers' Resources • Teaching Ideas • Busy Teachers' Website • Teachers' Hub •
│  MidLink Websites • The Educator's Toolkit • Sites For Teachers • A OK Teacher Stuff •
│  Educator's Reference Desk • Links for Elementary Educators • Teaching That Makes
│  Sense • Alfy's Playground • Cyber Bee Curriculum Ideas • Teachers First • The
│  Learning Page • Kim's Korner for Teacher Talk • Websites from Teaching Tips • Dewey
│  Browse • Virtual Teacher • Ed Sightings • The Franklin Institute On-Line • My
│  SchoolHouse • Web Schooling • ABC Teach • TEAMS Electronic Classrooms • Can
│  Teach • Get Smarter: The Real Challenge • ETTC's Greatest Hits (Burlington Cty) •
│  Kids Excellent Web Links (KEWL) • Room 108 Links • Web Tools for Teachers • Free
│  Things for Educators • Project Interactivate • Marco Polo Resources • Teaching
│  Resources from Laura Candler • Theme Units and On-Line Activities • Ed Helper • Ten
│  Games for Classroom Fun • Links for Teachers • Teacher Templates and Resources •
│  The Creative Teaching Website • Mrs. Seagrave's Quest and Thematic Units • Real-time
│  Data Websites • Interactive Lessons by Grade Level • I Love That Teaching Idea •
│  Classroom Activities • About School • The Inquiry Page • Instant Access Treasure
│  Chest •City Technology • Understanding the Common Essential Learnings • 42 Explore
│  • The Academy of Curriculum Exchange • Daily News Quiz • Brainchild Online Testing •
│  The Study Stack • Test Preparation Workbooks • Big News For Kids • Teacher Xpress
│  • Teach the Children Well Resources • Study Island
│                                                              │
└─────────────────────────────────────────────────────────────┘
```

• About Sue LeBeau •

Sue LeBeau has over 30 years of experience teaching in the elementary and middle school grades. She holds a Doctor of Education degree in Organizational Leadership in Instructional Technology, a Master of Arts Degree in Instructional Technology, a Master of Education degree, and a Bachelor of Arts degree in Elementary Education.

Dr. LeBeau is the recipient of the Teacher Recognition Award from Johns Hopkins University for 2001. She was also the recipient of the Technology Fellowship: Mentoring and Modeling Program for Monmouth County from the State of New Jersey for the 2001-2002 school year, where she trained teachers across the state on how to integrate technology in the classroom.

Dr. LeBeau is presently a Technology/Distance Learning Advisor for the Long Branch School District in New Jersey.

Resource 12.2

Two "Must See" Web Sites

Education World   **www.educationworld.com**

Education World is an excellent site for teachers. Subtitled *The Educator's Best Friend*, it could be your best resource on the Internet. There are six major divisions: *Lesson Planning, Administrator's Desk, School Issues, Professional Development, Technology Integration*, and *More Resources*. Articles here change often, so check the site daily or weekly. There is a *Joke of the Day, Quote of the Day*, and *Classroom Management Tip of the Day*. Also included are *Article Archives, Subject Resources, Specialties, Reference Center*, and *Featured Programs*. In the *Reference Center* you can subscribe to their newsletters, which will come to you weekly in your e-mail. Another weekly feature is Techtorials -- step-by-step instructions on using some aspect of technology in the regular classroom. These are short, practical, and educationally sound, providing classroom teachers with simple, straightforward tips you can use today! Techtorials deal with topics related to software applications, Internet use, computer maintenance and troubleshooting, special interest technology, and more--with a strong focus on the beginning or reluctant computer user.

An important part of the site contains articles they have published. A search engine takes you to the thousands of articles that have been published at **Education World**. Each article also contains links to related sites on the WWW.

Refdesk   **www.refdesk.com**

Their motto says it all: "The single best source for facts on the Net." This is truly the grand-daddy of all the web's reference sites. The site's major areas include Reference Resources, Headline News, Facts at a Glance, Facts Search Desk, Help and Advisor, Current News/Weather/Business/Sports, Top Reference Tools, and Subject Categories. The mindboggling scope of this site can only be eluded to (7,500 sites for facts, all newspapers on the web--USA and worldwide, 300+ quick research sites, and more).

"Refdesk is only about indexing quality Internet sites and assisting visitors in navigating these sites. At Refdesk that is all that counts and that is all that will ever count."

Chapter 13

Teaching in New Jersey

Name_____

CLASS REFLECTIONS - Teaching in New Jersey

....

Date:_____   Topic:_____

Description:

_____

_____

_____

_____

_____

Analysis:

_____

_____

_____

_____

_____

_____

Future Impact:

_____

_____

_____

_____

_____

_____

Date:_____   Topic:_____

Description:

_____

_____

_____

_____

_____

Analysis:

_____

_____

_____

_____

_____

Future Impact:

_____

_____

_____

_____

_____

Activity 13.1 - Review for Chapter 13

I. Clearly explain or define the following terms, concepts, or acronyms.

- Certificate of Eligibility (CE):

- Certificate of Eligibility with Advanced Standing (CEAS):

- County Substitute License:

- instructional endorsement:

- NJDOE:

- Provisional License:

- reciprocity:

- Standard License:

Name_____

Activity 13.2 - Returning As A Teacher

Scenario: You have graduated with a teaching degree in the subject area/grade level that you sought. While in the process of looking for a teaching job you learned that there is a vacancy at a school you attended for the exact subject area/grade level you desire.

Task: To assist you in deciding whether you want to apply for this position, you are going to list the pros and cons regarding several factors related to this job.

FACTOR	PROS	CONS
Teachers		
Students		

Administration		
Parents		
Neighborhood		
School District		

186

Resource 13.1

New Jersey's Three-Step
Certification Process for Novice Educators

STEP 1: **Establishing eligibility – Certificate of Eligibility and Certificate of Eligibility with Advanced Standing**

Certificate of Eligibility (CE): a credential with lifetime validity issued to persons who have completed a degree program of academic study and the applicable test requirements for certification. The CE permits the applicant to seek and accept employment in positions requiring certification.

- or -

Certificate of Eligibility with Advanced Standing (CEAS): a credential with lifetime validity issued to persons who have completed a degree program of academic study and the applicable test requirements and traditional professional preparation programs for certification. The CEAS permits the applicant to seek and accept employment in positions requiring certification.

STEP 2: **Legalizing Employment and Induction – Provisional Certificate**

Provisional Certificate: a two-year certificate issued to candidates who have met the requirements for initial employment (holder of a CE or CEAS) and are employed and part of a state-approved district training program or residency leading to standard certification.

STEP 3: **Becoming Permanently Certified – Standard Certification**

Standard Certificate: a permanent certificate issued to persons who have met all certification requirements.

Requirements for a Standard Instructional Certificate

1. Bachelor's degree from a regionally accredited college or university.

2. A baccalaureate degree, post-baccalaureate program or advanced degree cumulative grade point average (GPA) of at least 2.50, when a 4.0 equals an A grade for candidates graduating prior to September 1, 2004; a GPA of at least 2.75 for candidates graduating September 1, 2004 or later.

3. Passing score in Praxis II/NTE Programs Specialty Area test(s) for secondary teaching, the Elementary Education: Content Knowledge for elementary teachers.

4. Completion of a major in the liberal arts or sciences for elementary education. Completion of a major in the subject teaching field for an initial endorsement in a subject teaching field, except for vocational industrial certification. For additional endorsements, completion of at least 30 semester hours in a coherent major in the subject teaching field.

5. Successful completion of one of the following:

    • the Provisional Teacher Program (induction/mentoring for alternate route or traditionally prepared first-year teachers)

    - or -

    • a state approved college teacher preparation program and one year of full time teaching under a valid state license.

(Source: NJDOE)

Resource 13.2

New Jersey Department of Education Web Site
Licensing (May 2005)
[www.nj.gov/njded/educators/license]

New licensing regulations, N.J.A.C. 6A:9, were adopted by the New Jersey State Board of Education, effective January 20, 2004. Below are links to key parts of New Jersey's certification system.

Effective November 1, 2004, the online Teacher Certification Information System (TCIS) is available to the public.

If you obtained your certification prior to 1988, it is likely that your date of birth is not in the current database. Therefore, you will not be able to register as a new user at the present time.

CAREERS IN EDUCATION

- NJ Hire
    NJ Hire is a one-stop information and referral recruitment center for individuals who may be interested in a teaching career.

- **Troops to Teachers**
    The Troops to Teachers program is a federally funded program that provides assistance to military personnel who express an interest in teaching in New Jersey. For information about the Troops to Teachers program, please contact tttnj@doe.state.nj.us .

- **Higher Education Quality Initiatives / Professional Education Licensure Programs**
    Prospective teacher education candidates and others are invited to view education licensure preparation programs offered by New Jersey's colleges and universities at
    http://www.nj.gov/njded/aps/heqi/licensure.htm.

TEACHER CERTIFICATION INFORMATION SYSTEM (TCIS)

- USER MANUAL FOR ONLINE TEACHER CERTIFICATION INFORMATION SYSTEM (TCIS)
    This manual is required in order to fully understand and use the online TCIS process. To download and print this manual, you will need the free Adobe Acrobat Reader.

- APPLICANT CHECKLIST
    This checklist has been designed as an aid to facilitate applying for state certification

- USE THE ONLINE TEACHER CERTIFICATION INFORMATION SYSTEM (TCIS).
    - Create a user account
    - View and update your account information
    - View the status of your applications for certification
    - View your New Jersey educator certificates
    - View your certification test results (Praxis, SLLS)
    - Start your credential application process online
    - Update your education history and work experience
    - Complete a name change
    - Apply for a duplicate certificate

- CERTIFICATION IN NEW JERSEY AN EDUCATOR'S GUIDE, SCHOOL YEAR 2004-2005 (321 kb PDF)
    Requirements and process for certification, including Provisional Teacher/Alternate Route certification, Administrator and SAC Residency programs, and a list of all subject areas ("endorsements") for certificates.

- CERTIFICATION AND ENDORSEMENTS

- LICENSING CODE

- TEST REQUIREMENTS FOR LICENSURE IN NEW JERSEY

- DEGREE EQUIVALENCY FOR STUDIES COMPLETED IN FOREIGN COUNTRIES

- CHECK THE STATUS OF AN APPLICATION FOR CERTIFICATION

- FEE SCHEDULE (16 kb PDF)

- FORMS (PDF)
    - Non-Citizen Oath and Affadavit
    - Oath of Allegiance / Verification of Accuracy
    - Affadavit for Intent to Become a Citizen/Noncitizen Renewal
    - Verification of Program Completion
    - Notarized Statement of Certificate Loss
    - Date of Birth Correction
    - Social Security Number Record Change Request

To Request an application or information:
Call: (609) 292-2070. This number is available 24 hours per day, seven days per week and provides recorded information. To speak directly to a staff person, please call between the hours of 3:00 p.m. and 7:00 p.m. Monday through Friday.

Resource 13.3

New Jersey School 2004 Report Card
Washington Township High School

COUNTY: GLOUCESTER
DISTRICT: WASHINGTON TWP
Staff Information

- **Student/Administrator Ratio**
  Numbers of students per administrator.

	School	State Average
2001-02	265.0	180.8
2002-03	332.2	58.2
2003-04	308.8	185.1

- **Student/Faculty Ratio**
  Numbers of students per faculty member.

	School	State Average
2001-02	11.8	11.5
2002-03	11.5	11.5
2003-04	12.2	11.6

- **Faculty Attendance Rate**
  Percentage of faculty present on average each day.

	School	State Average
2001-02	96.1	95.6
2002-03	96.1	96.4
2003-04	95.1	96.2

- **Faculty Turnover Rate**
  Percentage of faculty who entered & left the school during the school year.

	School	State Average
2003-04	6.7%	7.2%

- **Teacher Information**
  Percentage of teachers teaching with emergency or conditional certificates.

	District	State
2002-03	0.3%	2.7%
2003-04	0.8%	3.7%

• Faculty and Administrator Credentials

Percentage of faculty and administrators possessing a bachelor's, master's, or doctoral degree.

	BA/BS	MA/MS	PhD/EdD
2001-02	67.0%	33.0%	0.0%
2002-03	66.4%	33.2%	0.4%
2003-04	68.7%	30.6%	0.8%

• National Board Certification

Number of teachers applying for and receiving certification.

	School	District	State
2001-02	0.0	0.0	3.0
2002-03	0.0	0.0	15.0
2003-04	0.0	1.0	55.0

<u>There are three essential components of a highly qualified teacher in accordance with the No Child Left Behind (NCLB) Act</u>:

* Hold at least a bachelor's degree;

* Be fully certified/licensed by New Jersey; and

* Demonstrate competence in each of the core academic subjects in which the teacher teaches.

<u>Teachers can demonstrate competence in the subject(s) they teach by either</u>:

* Passing a rigorous state test or completing an academic major, graduate degree, coursework equivalent to an undergraduate academic major, or national certification or credentialing; OR

* Meeting the requirements of the NJ High, Objective Uniform State Evaluation (HOUSE) Standard.

(Source: NJDOE)

Resource 13.4

Formative Evaluation Form for All
First-Year (Provisional) Teachers

The following formative evaluation instrument is completed for all first-year (provisional) teachers after the first ten (10) and twenty (20) weeks of teaching. A copy is sent to the New Jersey Department of Education, a copy is retained by the school district, and a copy is provided to the teacher.

Key: O = Outstanding   S = Satisfactory   N = Needs Improvement
      U = Unsatisfactory NA = Not Applicable When Observed

I. Curriculum, Instruction, and Assessment

Does the provisional teacher demonstrate the skills and knowledge to make effective decisions regarding:

    What is taught?
    How it is taught?
    How to assess the learning outcome?

            <u>The Provisional Teacher demonstrates the ability to</u>:

O S N U NA   A. Set clear objectives for each lesson

O S N U NA   B. Present information at levels appropriate to students

O S N U NA   C. Develop appropriate learning activities

O S N U NA   D. Provide clear instructions

O S N U NA   E. Develop educational experiences with opportunities for students to make decisions

O S N U NA   F. Pace and sequence instruction appropriately

O S N U NA   G. Intersperse questions to check for understanding

O S N U NA   H. Utilize technology as a teaching tool to enhance instruction

O S N U NA   I. Monitor the progress of students

O S N U NA   J. Provide feedback to students

O S N U NA   K. Use standardized tests and interpret results

O S N U NA   L. Develop and use other forms of assessment

O S N U NA   M. Appropriately use textbooks and teacher's guides

O S N U NA   N. Utilize techniques and materials for fostering the development of reading and language arts skills in daily lesson planning

II. Student Learning and Development

Does the provisional teacher demonstrate the skills and knowledge to make effective decisions regarding:

> How to meet the needs of children being taught?
> How to create an optimal environment for student learning and development?

> The Provisional Teacher demonstrates effective decision making and techniques to:

O S N U NA   A. Develop student interest and motivation

O S N U NA   B. Prevent classroom disruption

O S N U NA   C. Create an optimum environment for student learning and Development

O S N U NA   D. Adapt instruction to meet individual differences

O S N U NA   E. Foster cooperative and group learning

O S N U NA   F. Assist students in using technology as an aid to their Learning

III. Classroom and School

Does the provisional teacher demonstrate the skills and knowledge to make effective decisions regarding:

How to select effective teaching strategies?
How to function as a member of school and community?

<u>The Provisional Teacher demonstrates the skills and knowledge to:</u>

O S N U NA   A. Function effectively and responsibly within the bureaucratic and social structure of the educational system

O S N U NA   B. Allocate instructional time appropriately

O S N U NA   C. Set priorities

O S N U NA   D. Utilize a variety of questioning techniques

O S N U NA   E. Provide opportunity for appropriate independent work

O S N U NA   F. Provide all students with sufficient opportunity for successful practice

_____

Commendations:

Recommendations For Improvement:

_____	_____
Chairperson, Support Team	Date Evaluated
_____	_____
Provisional Teacher	Date Reviewed

Appendix

Student Information Form
(This information is provided for the professor's use only.)

Class Day(s)_____and Time_____

Name:_____
      (PRINT)   (Last Name)   (First Name)   (M.I.)

Academic Standing: ___Freshman ___Sophomore ___Junior ___Senior

Education Area/Major:_____

Phone Numbers: On-campus or local:_____

                 Home:_____

                 Work:_____

E-Mail Address:_____

Classes you are taking this semester:

    1._____

    2._____

    3._____

    4._____

    5._____

    6._____

Teaching: An Introduction to the Profession
Class Observation Notes

Directions: Use this form to record information that you will refer to when **word processing** your report of the class observation. Use a new blank form for each observation. Attach your "observation notes" forms to your final reports.

School Name_____

School Address_____

Teacher_____ Grade Level(s)_____

Subject_____ No. of Students_____

Lesson Topic_____

1. What did the teacher do that exhibited <u>planning</u> for this class? (Look for a lesson plan, handouts, overhead transparencies, posters, bulletin boards, models, manipulatives, teaching aids, PowerPoint files, books or other text, tools, equipment, etc. What did the teacher do <u>prior</u> to the lesson to make it a success?)

2. What did the teacher do to <u>maintain control</u> of student behavior during the class? (Here, we mean classroom management. Were students on task during instruction? What did the teacher do to assure this? Were class rules and procedures posted in the classroom? What was the general tone of the classroom during instruction? – enthusiasm, boredom, anxiety, happiness, anger, disillusionment, supportive and cooperative, competitive, etc.)

3. What did the teacher do that demonstrates his/her <u>knowledge, dispositions, and performance</u> in the content area(s) of the lesson? (How did the teacher demonstrate knowledge about the lesson's topic(s)? How did the teacher exhibit enthusiasm and a passion for the lesson's content and learning experiences? How did the teacher demonstrate or model the learning activities for the students? Was the lesson successful based upon the teacher's performance? Why?)

4. What did the teacher do to achieve <u>student involvement</u> during the class? (Describe what the students did during the lesson. What level of involvement did the students exhibit? Detail their activities – passive? active? Did the students participate in their own learning? ...learning of peers? Did the teacher create a competitive or cooperative environment? etc. Respond by describing how the **teacher** got the students to be involved.)

5. What types of <u>instructional tools</u> did the teacher and students use during instruction? (Overhead projector, transparencies, PowerPoint software and projector, computer, bulletin board, handouts, textbooks, models, chalkboard, whiteboard, "smartboard," equipment, visual presenter/document camera, TV, videotape, CD, DVD, audio equipment, camcorder, etc.)

6. Other Comments:

Teaching: An Introduction to the Profession
Class Observation Notes

Directions: Use this form to record information that you will refer to when **word processing** your report of the class observation. Use a new blank form for each observation. Attach your "observation notes" forms to your final reports.

School Name_____

School Address_____

Teacher_____ Grade Level(s)_____

Subject_____ No. of Students_____

Lesson Topic_____

1. What did the teacher do that exhibited <u>planning</u> for this class? (Look for a lesson plan, handouts, overhead transparencies, posters, bulletin boards, models, manipulatives, teaching aids, PowerPoint files, books or other text, tools, equipment, etc. What did the teacher do <u>prior</u> to the lesson to make it a success?)

2. What did the teacher do to <u>maintain control</u> of student behavior during the class? (Here, we mean classroom management. Were students on task during instruction? What did the teacher do to assure this? Were class rules and procedures posted in the classroom? What was the general tone of the classroom during instruction? – enthusiasm, boredom, anxiety, happiness, anger, disillusionment, supportive and cooperative, competitive, etc.)

3. What did the teacher do that demonstrates his/her <u>knowledge, dispositions, and performance</u> in the content area(s) of the lesson? (How did the teacher demonstrate knowledge about the lesson's topic(s)? How did the teacher exhibit enthusiasm and a passion for the lesson's content and learning experiences? How did the teacher demonstrate or model the learning activities for the students? Was the lesson successful based upon the teacher's performance? Why?)

4. What did the teacher do to achieve <u>student involvement</u> during the class? (Describe what the students did during the lesson. What level of involvement did the students exhibit? Detail their activities – passive? active? Did the students participate in their own learning? ...learning of peers? Did the teacher create a competitive or cooperative environment? etc. Respond by describing how the **teacher** got the students to be involved.)

5. What types of <u>instructional tools</u> did the teacher and students use during instruction? (Overhead projector, transparencies, PowerPoint software and projector, computer, bulletin board, handouts, textbooks, models, chalkboard, whiteboard, "smartboard," equipment, visual presenter/document camera, TV, videotape, CD, DVD, audio equipment, camcorder, etc.)

6. Other Comments:

Teaching: An Introduction to the Profession
Class Observation Notes

Directions: Use this form to record information that you will refer to when **word processing** your report of the class observation. Use a new blank form for each observation. Attach your "observation notes" forms to your final reports.

School Name_____

School Address_____

Teacher_____ Grade Level(s)_____

Subject_____ No. of Students_____

Lesson Topic_____

1. What did the teacher do that exhibited <u>planning</u> for this class? (Look for a lesson plan, handouts, overhead transparencies, posters, bulletin boards, models, manipulatives, teaching aids, PowerPoint files, books or other text, tools, equipment, etc. What did the teacher do <u>prior</u> to the lesson to make it a success?)

2. What did the teacher do to <u>maintain control</u> of student behavior during the class? (Here, we mean classroom management. Were students on task during instruction? What did the teacher do to assure this? Were class rules and procedures posted in the classroom? What was the general tone of the classroom during instruction? – enthusiasm, boredom, anxiety, happiness, anger, disillusionment, supportive and cooperative, competitive, etc.)

3. What did the teacher do that demonstrates his/her <u>knowledge, dispositions, and performance</u> in the content area(s) of the lesson? (How did the teacher demonstrate knowledge about the lesson's topic(s)? How did the teacher exhibit enthusiasm and a passion for the lesson's content and learning experiences? How did the teacher demonstrate or model the learning activities for the students? Was the lesson successful based upon the teacher's performance? Why?)

4. What did the teacher do to achieve <u>student involvement</u> during the class? (Describe what the students did during the lesson. What level of involvement did the students exhibit? Detail their activities – passive? active? Did the students participate in their own learning? ...learning of peers? Did the teacher create a competitive or cooperative environment? etc. Respond by describing how the **teacher** got the students to be involved.)

5. What types of <u>instructional tools</u> did the teacher and students use during instruction? (Overhead projector, transparencies, PowerPoint software and projector, computer, bulletin board, handouts, textbooks, models, chalkboard, whiteboard, "smartboard," equipment, visual presenter/document camera, TV, videotape, CD, DVD, audio equipment, camcorder, etc.)

6. Other Comments:

Teaching: An Introduction to the Profession
Class Observation Notes

Directions: Use this form to record information that you will refer to when **word processing** your report of the class observation. Use a new blank form for each observation. Attach your "observation notes" forms to your final reports.

School Name_____

School Address_____

Teacher_____ Grade Level(s)_____

Subject_____ No. of Students_____

Lesson Topic_____

1. What did the teacher do that exhibited <u>planning</u> for this class? (Look for a lesson plan, handouts, overhead transparencies, posters, bulletin boards, models, manipulatives, teaching aids, PowerPoint files, books or other text, tools, equipment, etc. What did the teacher do <u>prior</u> to the lesson to make it a success?)

2. What did the teacher do to <u>maintain control</u> of student behavior during the class? (Here, we mean classroom management. Were students on task during instruction? What did the teacher do to assure this? Were class rules and procedures posted in the classroom? What was the general tone of the classroom during instruction? – enthusiasm, boredom, anxiety, happiness, anger, disillusionment, supportive and cooperative, competitive, etc.)

3. What did the teacher do that demonstrates his/her <u>knowledge, dispositions, and performance</u> in the content area(s) of the lesson? (How did the teacher demonstrate knowledge about the lesson's topic(s)? How did the teacher exhibit enthusiasm and a passion for the lesson's content and learning experiences? How did the teacher demonstrate or model the learning activities for the students? Was the lesson successful based upon the teacher's performance? Why?)

4. What did the teacher do to achieve <u>student involvement</u> during the class? (Describe what the students did during the lesson. What level of involvement did the students exhibit? Detail their activities – passive? active? Did the students participate in their own learning? ...learning of peers? Did the teacher create a competitive or cooperative environment? etc. Respond by describing how the **teacher** got the students to be involved.)

5. What types of <u>instructional tools</u> did the teacher and students use during instruction? (Overhead projector, transparencies, PowerPoint software and projector, computer, bulletin board, handouts, textbooks, models, chalkboard, whiteboard, "smartboard," equipment, visual presenter/document camera, TV, videotape, CD, DVD, audio equipment, camcorder, etc.)

6. Other Comments:

Teaching: An Introduction to the Profession
Class Observation Notes

Directions: Use this form to record information that you will refer to when **word processing** your report of the class observation. Use a new blank form for each observation. Attach your "observation notes" forms to your final reports.

School Name_____

School Address_____

Teacher_____ Grade Level(s)_____

Subject_____ No. of Students_____

Lesson Topic_____

1. What did the teacher do that exhibited <u>planning</u> for this class? (Look for a lesson plan, handouts, overhead transparencies, posters, bulletin boards, models, manipulatives, teaching aids, PowerPoint files, books or other text, tools, equipment, etc. What did the teacher do <u>prior</u> to the lesson to make it a success?)

2. What did the teacher do to <u>maintain control</u> of student behavior during the class? (Here, we mean classroom management. Were students on task during instruction? What did the teacher do to assure this? Were class rules and procedures posted in the classroom? What was the general tone of the classroom during instruction? – enthusiasm, boredom, anxiety, happiness, anger, disillusionment, supportive and cooperative, competitive, etc.)

3. What did the teacher do that demonstrates his/her <u>knowledge, dispositions, and performance</u> in the content area(s) of the lesson? (How did the teacher demonstrate knowledge about the lesson's topic(s)? How did the teacher exhibit enthusiasm and a passion for the lesson's content and learning experiences? How did the teacher demonstrate or model the learning activities for the students? Was the lesson successful based upon the teacher's performance? Why?)

4. What did the teacher do to achieve <u>student involvement</u> during the class? (Describe what the students did during the lesson. What level of involvement did the students exhibit? Detail their activities – passive? active? Did the students participate in their own learning? ...learning of peers? Did the teacher create a competitive or cooperative environment? etc. Respond by describing how the **teacher** got the students to be involved.)

5. What types of <u>instructional tools</u> did the teacher and students use during instruction? (Overhead projector, transparencies, PowerPoint software and projector, computer, bulletin board, handouts, textbooks, models, chalkboard, whiteboard, "smartboard," equipment, visual presenter/document camera, TV, videotape, CD, DVD, audio equipment, camcorder, etc.)

6. Other Comments:

Teaching: An Introduction to the Profession
Class Observation Notes

Directions: Use this form to record information that you will refer to when **word processing** your report of the class observation. Use a new blank form for each observation. Attach your "observation notes" forms to your final reports.

School Name_____

School Address_____

Teacher_____ Grade Level(s)_____

Subject_____ No. of Students_____

Lesson Topic_____

1. What did the teacher do that exhibited <u>planning</u> for this class? (Look for a lesson plan, handouts, overhead transparencies, posters, bulletin boards, models, manipulatives, teaching aids, PowerPoint files, books or other text, tools, equipment, etc. What did the teacher do <u>prior</u> to the lesson to make it a success?)

2. What did the teacher do to <u>maintain control</u> of student behavior during the class? (Here, we mean classroom management. Were students on task during instruction? What did the teacher do to assure this? Were class rules and procedures posted in the classroom? What was the general tone of the classroom during instruction? – enthusiasm, boredom, anxiety, happiness, anger, disillusionment, supportive and cooperative, competitive, etc.)

3. What did the teacher do that demonstrates his/her <u>knowledge, dispositions, and performance</u> in the content area(s) of the lesson? (How did the teacher demonstrate knowledge about the lesson's topic(s)? How did the teacher exhibit enthusiasm and a passion for the lesson's content and learning experiences? How did the teacher demonstrate or model the learning activities for the students? Was the lesson successful based upon the teacher's performance? Why?)

4. What did the teacher do to achieve <u>student involvement</u> during the class? (Describe what the students did during the lesson. What level of involvement did the students exhibit? Detail their activities – passive? active? Did the students participate in their own learning? ...learning of peers? Did the teacher create a competitive or cooperative environment? etc. Respond by describing how the **teacher** got the students to be involved.)

5. What types of <u>instructional tools</u> did the teacher and students use during instruction? (Overhead projector, transparencies, PowerPoint software and projector, computer, bulletin board, handouts, textbooks, models, chalkboard, whiteboard, "smartboard," equipment, visual presenter/document camera, TV, videotape, CD, DVD, audio equipment, camcorder, etc.)

6. Other Comments:

Observation Symposium Worksheet

<u>**Individual Activity Directions:**</u>

Describe the best example of each of the following five elements that you encountered when doing your observations.

Element 1 - Best example of <u>Planning</u>.

Element 2 - Best strategy to <u>Maintain Control of the Class.</u>

Element 3 - Best example that demonstrated <u>Knowledge of the Content Area</u>.

Element 4 - Best example of <u>Student Involvement</u>.

Element 5 - Best example of the <u>Use of an Instructional Tool</u>.

<u>Group Activity Directions</u>:

- Record your group's assigned element number_____

- Meet with your group and share the idea you have identified for your assigned element.

- Select the three best ideas.

- The group will make a brief presentation to the class.